LABVIEW – MORE LCOD

MORE LABVIEW COMPONENT ORIENTED DESIGN

ROB MASKELL

MASTEC LTD

Published by MasTec NZ
Contact: lcodcoc@gmail.com

A catalogue record for this book is available from the National Library of New Zealand.
ISBN 978-0-473-65968-4 (paperback)
ISBN 978-0-473-65969-1 (EPUB)

CONTENTS

PREFACE

LabVIEW Component Oriented Design (LCOD) is a method that uses several simple "Design Rules" that can be helpful in programming LabVIEW applications.

I have been using some of the LCOD methods for over 30 years. In 2010 I started writing about this LCOD experience on my website and eventually developed some programming notes on LCOD. This sat for a while until I finally edited and expanded them into this book.

Whether you are a new LabVIEW programmer or an old seasoned one like me, the quest always remains the same, building better programs with our "favourite software tool > LabVIEW".

The aim of this book is to offer some guidance and help in achieving this.

I have been programming and using many design methods and languages for over half a century. In 1988, I wrote the first LabVIEW & LabWindows training courses for Europe.

I have trained over 3000 people on how to program in LabVIEW.

This book is about the evolution of my design work using LabVIEW LCOD over the last 35 years. I started working on this LCOD methodology, unknowingly and naturally in 1987 in my first LabVIEW programs. It developed very slowly from there. What's 35 years?

Just a heads up: in many pages of the book, you will find the abbreviation "COC". Don't panic, it is not "Clash of the Clans". "COC" serves as an abbreviation for the term used on many pages, namely "Cluster of Constants". Pronounce it C – O – Cs : no, not the other way.

"Cluster of Constants" or COCs are at the heart of this book. They may, after a while, invoke mental pictures and even dreams.

COC may even become LV jargon, an acronym. How is that COC coming along?? Is it a Type Def? Definitely make it a Type Def!

Another term used throughout the book: when you read "Component", think "Oh yes, a special type of LabVIEW SubVI or a LCOD state engine". These three terms Component, SubVI and LCOD state engine may be used alternately throughout the book.

This book may be the "final hurrah" of an older LabVIEW groupie, almost!

A big thank you to Jeff Kodosky and his development teams over the years before I go. It has always been a great delight to play with your creation, considering the software tools we were using before it came along.

Thank you also to Jim Truchard and NI for driving the Virtual Instruments and LabVIEW products to market.

And just to complete my professional work cycle, recently I have found a young engineer to continue with my LabVIEW creations who will probably markedly improve them.

Enjoy the book.

INTRODUCTION

Just to make this book a little more fun, I have included some chapters of my experiences with various technologies from the 1960s to the present. It started with a 1967 PDP 8i that was first used to provide biomedical instrumentation solutions and then the newer evolving technology that was used to meet requirements in many university research fields, then later industrial test, automation, instrumentation, T&M, agriculture, horticulture, marine, military calibration and repair, also some embedding, sensors and a little on teaching LabVIEW worldwide.

abbreviation >> LV = LabVIEW
abbreviation >> COC = Cluster of Constants
abbreviation >> LCOD = LabVIEW Component Oriented Design

DESIGN CONCEPTS AND METHODS OF LCOD PROGRAMS

Before the mid-1990s, this LCOD abbreviation did not exist, although I am sure some were playing with the concepts. Finally, in the mid-1990s, these concepts were made real and introduced in the book *A Software Engineering Approach to LabVIEW* by Jon Conway and Steve Watts.

It outlined the design concepts and methods of LCOD programs, with four main focuses:

1. Hidden Data
2. Abstraction
3. High Cohesion
4. Low Coupling

It is a great book and explains three of the focuses very well.

This present book shows a better way for "hidden data" and can become a companion and or an adjunct to the original book.

The book's purpose is to expand the understanding and use of LCOD.

Hidden Data

Hidden Data in this book means: removing constants from diagrams; in fact removing them from the program entirely, on to disk.

This book will show a graphical method to achieve hidden data: an important LabVIEW step. Over several chapters this new hidden data method will be expanded to completion. This new LCOD design method also develops into a full programming methodology.

Abstraction

Abstraction in this book means a programming methodology that takes concepts, data, information and ideas based in "computer" terminology and language, such as data types and formats, hardware descriptions, port #s, bit #s etc. and elevates those meanings to more meaningful "human" language word descriptions and concepts. Abstracting will allow a more human context into the program solution in the actual LabVIEW front panels, diagrams and data.

Abstraction promotes a language elevation or conversion to take place for clarity of meaning.

Examples of abstraction or language conversion or elevating meaning

- "Computer" words > Digital Output Port A has Bit # 1 True. The abstraction: in human words this becomes Water Pump #1 = ON

- Computer words > ADC Channel # 5 > Reading is 3 VDC. The abstraction: in human words becomes > Manometer # 1 Pressure = 2000 Pascals (by calibration).

To achieve these abstractions:

- LCOD usually uses Named State Engines (Components) (Nouns).
- LCOD State Engines Case Selectors are controlled by a series of enum constants as (verbs) (actions).

Enum Constants and Enum Controls

Abstraction happens in many places in LabVIEW. One example is inside a State Engine diagram, when the controlling enums, as (verbs), are wired to a Case Selector.

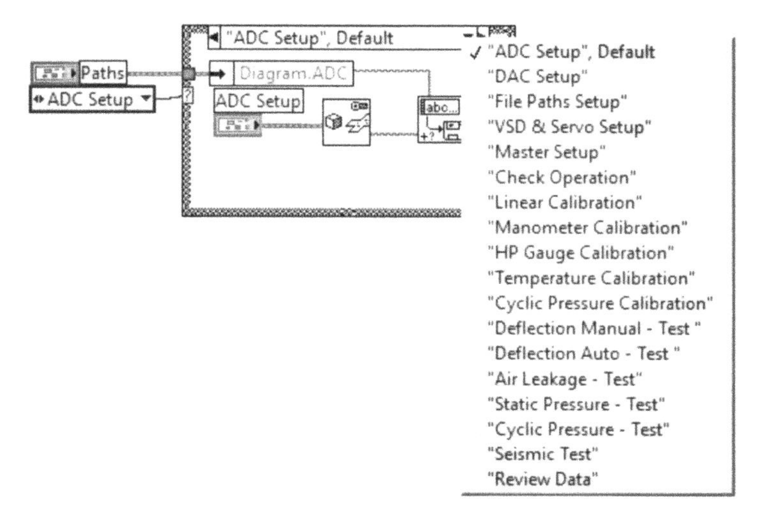

Enum abstraction

The "Text Data" in the enums that are wired to the Case Selector are now displayed in each individual case state's heading or label.

Abstracting is very helpful for the programmer, adding meaning and documentation to the diagram.

Cohesion

Cohesion in this book means: focused and singular-purpose SubVIs or Component, such as "Calibrate this sensor" or "do this type of test". Not combining those two tasks together in one SubVI. Cohesion is all about splitting or separating these types of combo SubVIs into separate focused, cohesive pieces for clarity and ease of maintenance.

Not doing half a computation in one SubVI and the rest in another SubVI.

Coupling

Coupling in this book means: Low/No Coupling throughout a LabVIEW diagram is imperative.

Coupling occurs between SubVIs in two ways, Code and Data.

Code Coupling

If there is a SubVIs used inside a program in two locations and you edit the SubVI in one part of the program to make it work correctly there but forget about the other location's use of the same SubVI, you immediately create an accidental coding coupling error. Whenever the SubVI runs in this forgotten location, it could result in I/O malfunction, data errors and the like. Great confusion can arise.

It is always better to create two separate SubVIs with different distinct names to stop accidental code coupling. Name them for their function, location and purpose. This makes each a private SubVI.

All the encouragement about "reuse" of SubVIs throughout a program may not always be totally beneficial. LabVIEW is very efficient in compiling small code size SubVIs.

Data Coupling

Data coupling is more common.

It is very easy for data coupling to get out of control. For example, it can happen when private data and public data usage becomes confused. private data in this book is data that only a single SubVI knows, uses and has access to. public data, on the other hand, is available to all SubVIs of a program. For instance, if two SubVIs share private data between them and the private data in one SubVI is modified to achieve a certain result, there will be a data coupling error when the other SubVI runs. This is especially true for calibration data and constants used in formulas.

OTHER AREAS OF FOCUS

I would like to add a couple more items to the list of four above for LCOD focus.

Public and Private Data

Continuing on with public and private data ideas. Program designs that separate public and private data correctly will often exhibit strong cohesion and low coupling naturally. Get the public and private data rules sorted and the program will become simpler and more stable.

Enums as Type Defs

Make all Enums into Type Defs (verbs). Use them everywhere but especially for driving the SubVI State Engine's Case Selectors.

Also do make all controls and indicators that are repeatedly used throughout the whole program into Type Defs.

This is especially true for complex front panel clusters of controls or indicators.

These Type Defs will create the consistent "look and feel" uniformity in the front panels.

Some examples:

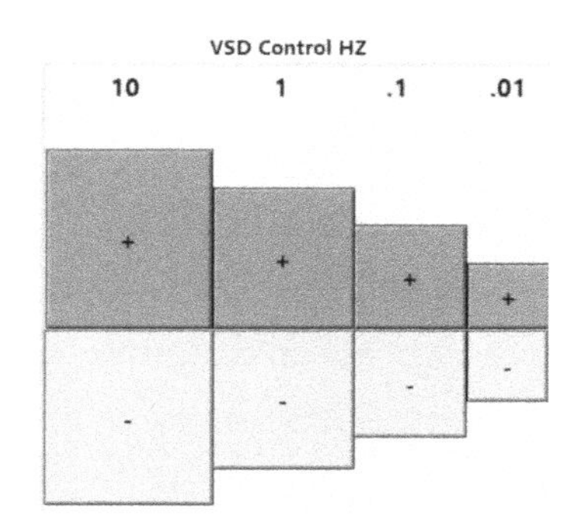

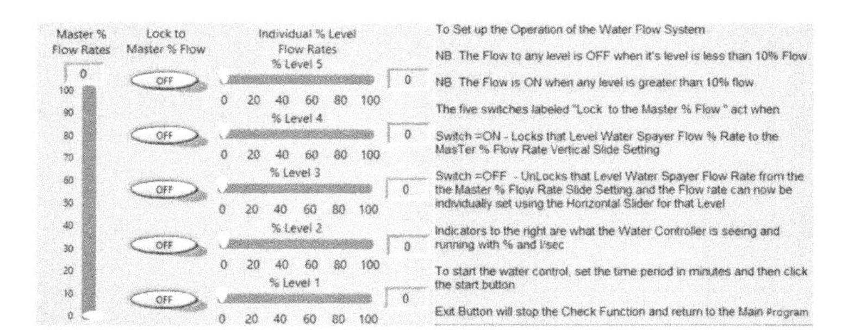

Cluster type definitions

These two Control examples are clusters.

Also, numeric, strings, booleans, arrays, charts and graphs that operators use, once sized, fonted, coloured and so on, need to be Type Defs.

As you will see later, all the Cluster of Constants or COCs used in the hidden data method are Type Defs. Type Defs take a little time to build, yet do it, as it will pay off handsomely.

These rules are especially applicable to large programs where you cannot hope to hold the details about all the SubVI's front panels, diagrams and data in your mind. Rely on Type Defs to manage a large part of it all for you. You will know you are globally winning in your design efforts when you change a Type Def and save it, and the computer sits for some time updating all the other copies throughout the program. Smile when this happens.

If you are building small programs, still use these development points, as someday you will build a big program and all the early training will pay off.

Programming Ecology

I call these ideas and methods "programming ecology", as the design is nurtured, kept clean and healthy. Take your time and don't short circuit the build; stay on cue and keep the design flow right through to the end.

Ecology. Go around and pick up all the garbage and clean up the mess so it can breathe.

This introduction, hopefully, will whet the appetite for some LCOD learning and fun.

CHAPTER 1

THOUGHTS ON AND EXPERIENCES OF LABVIEW PROGRAMMING

Focus:

- LabVIEW Program Design
- Using LCOD

The book uses a series of LabVIEW applications to demonstrate the LCOD methods.

All the applications panel and diagram snippets are from various versions of "Australian and New Zealand Standards" Windows, Walls, Doors, Roofs and Facade Industrial Testers.

The first example shown is a front panel for these types of industrial tester applications.

This front panel shows the main application's entry point for the operator at startup.

Notice the row of Tabs used.

These Tabs are used to hide developer front panel details from the operators.

At runtime all the Tabs disappear and the operator only sees the Main Tab.

The developer and commissioner have all the Tabs available as we will see how later.

You can if you choose, merge the Tab Control into the background by making the Tab Control transparent and making the fore and background the same colour. I usually do this but left them exposed for the book to highlight the Tab structure.

Also if you are working in an older LabVIEW like I am (LV 7.1.1), do not change the display resolution if you can help it as the Tab Control COC placements may get messed with, as you may find out. Newer LV versions may not do this.

And below, this application's main diagram, showing the first state name (Paths).

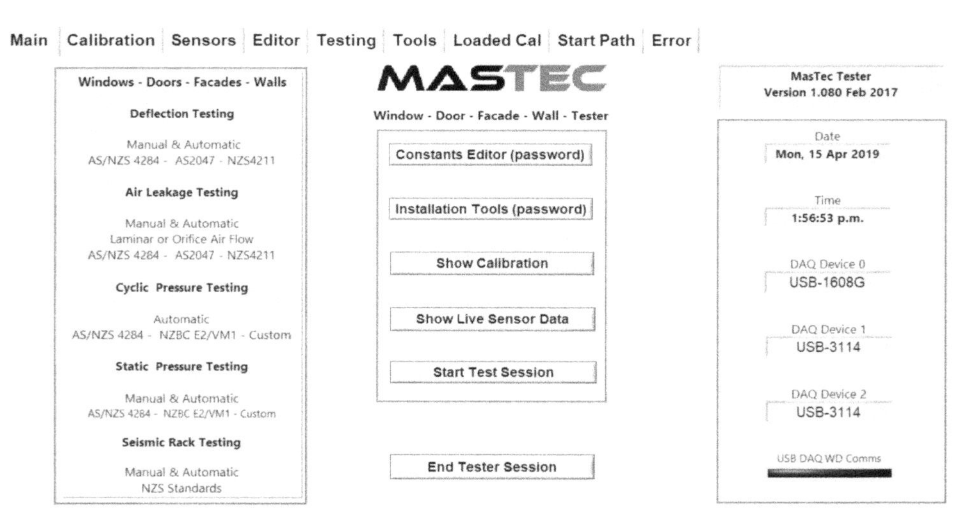

Main panel tabs

The shift registers are loaded with the applications "public data" in several configuration states.

This is a standard LabVIEW method used in many applications.

The diagrams states are controlled by Type Def enum constants.

Several files are opened in this “Paths” state.

The book will expand this simple design method into a new type of development framework using COC methods.

First though a little LabVIEW background info.

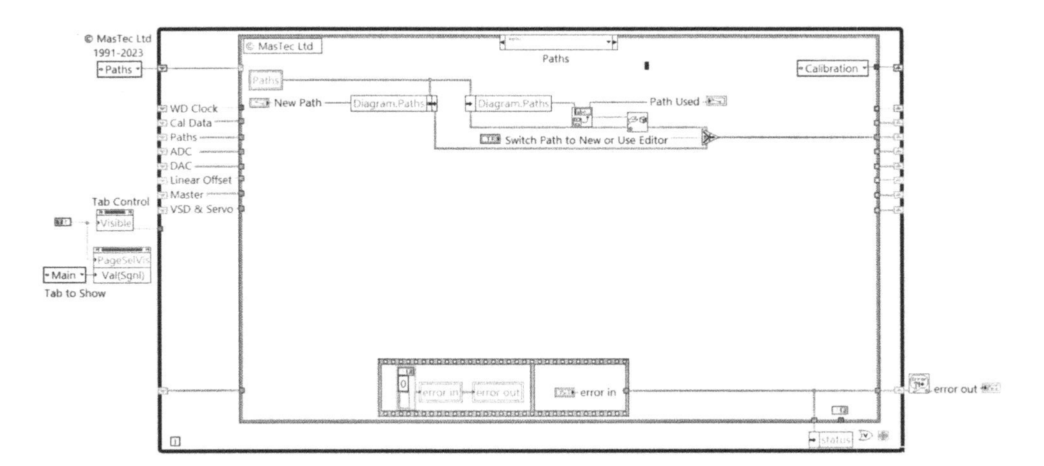

Main diagram framework

LABVIEW PROGRAMMING THOUGHTS AND EXPERIENCES

The great thing about LabVIEW with its Data Flow execution, is that it offers programmers such broad freedoms of expression, using the superb graphical development tools.

Having programmed in text code during the previous 20 years, I was hooked the first time I put the 3.5-inch LabVIEW Demo floppy disk in my new Mac SE. That was in mid-1987. I still have that Demo manual and floppy.

This great freedom of expression allows you to make an absolute mess of a programming; that is, if you do not follow any design methods.

Or

You can make sublime pictures that translate the design ideas and methods into great applications.

I have seen many examples of both approaches and maybe even made some myself. This is why LCOD is so important, as it may stop the mess and reckless programming. Large programs can become chaotic without design. LCOD can help considerably, as it keeps the focus tight and allows a naturally expanding method.

My programming in Assembler, Fortran, Focal, Basic and Forth during the 1960s, 70s and 80s has been a great help in my LabVIEW work.

Forth especially required clarity of mind, tight succinct design, correct naming of words, building components, lexicons of functions, abstraction to the absolute max, clear pathways to build extensibility and on-your-toes development (fast and creative). LV also has all of this and much more.

Although greatly different, both Forth and LabVIEW have several commonalities: incremental compiling, very fast compiling, interactive development, and easy troubleshooting. Both encourage making little pieces (SubVI/Words) to create a solution that can be easily linked together to create bigger solutions. Both encourage specific solutions rather than generalised ones. Plus re-use.

People have been wrestling with how to build focused and specific LabVIEW programs since the beginning. In fact, if you look at LabVIEW discussion forums, a lot of the talk is about frameworks, structures and methods to control "How Not to Make a Mess" and instead create the sublime.

There are many excellent books that discuss all the gymnastics that are possible in LV; that is, making the complex tameable and simpler.

The books that I recommend to beginners to mid-level LV programmers like myself, are:

- A Software Engineering Approach to LabVIEW

- LabVIEW GUI — Essential Techniques
- LabVIEW Advanced Programming Techniques 2nd edition
- Learning LabVIEW 8
- The LabVIEW Style Book
- LabVIEW for Everyone — Graphical Programming made easy and fun (latest edition)

All these books, and many others, and their writers are superb and show you how to use all the LV tools and techniques well. A good number of real applications are presented and discussed. These authors are to be congratulated on the huge effort they have put into their professional careers and sharing it in their books to help us less-savvy or less-aware programmers to become better.

I watched from a distance as LabVIEW became more complex over the years and the need grew for more explanation of how to use it well. I have felt these explanations have good intentions and are probably essential and helpful to keep some form of order. However, there is still very little available on the simple design of programs. It seems very few are brave enough to stick their neck out and have a go on this subject. Be gentle.

Much of the discussions and training in LV are more about how to use all the bits, structures, templates, options, functions, interfacing and comms and only lightly touch on design methods.

When I program, I find it is easier to design and build a program that isn't complex. I use these LCOD methods to tame complexity.

The main rule in all LV things, for me, is to **"Stay Simple"**. If I see the programming design or build process getting complex, I look again and again and if it remains essential to be complex, I go hire a LabVIEW person who can work in a complex way.

However, often:

Complex = Lack of Understanding = Spec still needs more Dissection or Simplifying.

To that end and for many years now, I have recommended my LabVIEW students study the first of the books in the list: *A Software Engineering Approach to LabVIEW*. It has a load of great stuff in it to help you actually design, using LCOD, and to keep things simpler. It shows the ins and outs of LCOD: the LabVIEW Components which are special SubVIs and that are normally state engines.

A Software Engineering Approach to LabVIEW

Here is a very short summary of what this book on LabVIEW Component Oriented Design (LCOD) basically has in it.

This LCOD method brings to your programs.

- Increased cohesion
- Reduced coupling
- Data Hiding > "Hidden Data"
- Greater abstraction
- Better design
- Reuse
- Easier and automatic documentation
- Easier trouble shooting
- Better error handling
- Easier upgrade, reuse and expansion later

After years of development work in LabVIEW, I thought I had good design and build methods. However, in comparing my work with the LCOD method, I found I was somewhat close but needed to smarten up on some of the items, especially data hiding or "hidden data".

WHY USE DESIGN, ESPECIALLY LCOD?

Common problems in all programming languages

You may have built a program and when you got close to the end of development and the commissioning started, progressively the program became very hard and stubborn to complete, as continuous spurious errors or missing functionality started showing up. Cohesion and coupling issues also reared their ugly heads. You may have found that it has a compromised private and public data methodology. It often can become quite a nightmare.

If you have had a program like this, you will know that you often spend more time at the installation and commissioning cycle, fixing all the broken stuff and the mess that may arise, than on the total time of development of the program. This can be true even when using qualified programmers and excellent development tools.

Programmers often get it wrong due to the final design having undefined items or simple misunderstandings because of complexity issues, with elements not being broken down to simple, clear ideas.

The start of a project is not to be rushed into, just to get programming, but rather you should look deeper at what is required. Get a requirement spec, front panels sketches and data flows, then develop the design, look for simplification and commonalities and rework it until it is simpler and simpler. LCOD will help with this.

A simple test to check your programs design's worth and stability:

“A good clear design can be expanded without distorting the current program”.

Expansion of the program should flow from the original work's methods with ease.

Design clarity is number 1.

Where to start programming

Where to start programming, top or bottom, is always the big question. There are lots of books on this. The last chapter is devoted to team development and discussing this further.

With my method, it is a bit of both. Start defining and building the top level public data COCs for the user front panels, hardware definitions and configuration details even if it is rudimentary, make them Type Defs. This is the beginning of the public data available to the whole program. Design and build the Tab Control these COCs will reside in. Choose your main program structure, a state Engine or an Event engine of some sort, and start to build the loading of the COCs from disk as will be shown in this book.

For the workhorse components in the program, i.e. reading and controlling instrumentation or automation devices, I always start at the bottom, at the TCP Comms, Serial Comms, and DAQ I/O, and start to build abstraction layers wrapped around the hardware. This will start filling in the design of the COC public data at the top level. Build simple LCOD components that use the I/O hardware and abstract up to where a human operator will understand the front panel terms. This also sorts out the EUs (engineering units) with calibration factors and the units.

This bottom-up work also reassures you that you can actually drive the hardware and achieve the specification requirements.

As you do this bottom-up abstraction work, the required application's top level front panels and the main diagram framework to build the application in, will often pop out as obvious. The front panels layouts will naturally link to all the abstraction layers, presenting the data to the operator well.

Sorting out LV program issues with LCOD

Over the years I have looked at a large number of LV applications from other programmers. I sometimes get called in to clean up these programs and complete a difficult project, add more functionality, fix the design etc. "Make it run and then actually make it do what it is meant to do."

Common issues

- Loose cohesion — no focus in SubVIs
- Cross-coupling — in both public and private data
- Cross-coupling in code — fragments of the same stuff everywhere.
- Many SubVI or Components — with private data in public view
- Poor abstraction — sometimes none.
- Flat designs — huge diagrams
- Poor diagrams — design and layout
- Globals — causing code runaways or strange behaviours
- Type Defs and enums — little understanding
- Initialisation — haphazard or none
- No Hidden data methods — a static program locked in time
- Poor automatic diagram documentation
- None or poor documentation — if a diagram is built well, it is almost self-documenting.

LCOD can help with all of these issues, if used correctly, using a clear mind with confidence.

Get the fundamentals correct at the beginning, Top down > Main Tab control setup, the public data as COCs, the diagram design to sit the program in. Bottom up > Make sure the current IO hardware can actually do the job. Build the first LCOD component with abstraction. This will often help sort out what public data in COCs is required at the top level.

A LITTLE MORE ON HIDDEN DATA

Hidden data methods are not often discussed in LabVIEW blogs, texts, courses or books. I have seen some LV programmers try to use "ini files" for hidden data methods. However, ini files are not LabVIEW-centric ("not graphical") and are just a legacy method of code work.

Hidden data is an essential part of LCOD. It is "removing all constants from the diagrams" to files and "reloading them at run time".

How to achieve this "hidden data" method will be shown in detail in later chapters. The method is one of the four important parts of software design and there are some tricks to make it easier in LabVIEW.

In fact, LabVIEW can do hidden data better than any other programming method. That was a bold statement!

The decision to use this book's "hidden data" method can bring rapid improvement and transformation to the whole program. It helps to control your program design and keep it focused.

Benefits of using Hidden Data methods

- Insides of LV diagrams are cleaner (no constants)
- The program is now "not stuck in time" or constant bound; the constants can be changed outside the program with a constants file editor.
- The process and design of bringing the constants back into the diagram often create automatic documentation.
- Creating a stabilising design throughout the program.
- Updates or additions will just follow the hidden data LCOD design automatically.
- Easier support; poke your head in the diagram and come up to speed fast and easier.
- Making hidden data Type Defs, reduces the detail to remember while programming.
- For LabVIEW contractors, this adds the ease of modifications to the software, as much can be achieved with just changing the constants in the "hidden data" files. This means diagrams are not opened for

these types of changes, only a new "hidden data" file is edited and sent to the site, with no software changes, and it can be done while the application is running and the changes will take place immediately the next time that SubVI runs.
- By having private hidden data for each SubVI's diagram, the result is high cohesion (or component focus) and also it brings low data coupling, as other SubVIs do not ever see or use any other SubVIs' private hidden data or Hidden constants.
- It also makes debug/testing much easier because of no/low coupling issues.

That was just some encouragement to think about using this new LCOD hidden data method.

CHAPTER 2
TECHNOLOGY HISTORY 1

PDP 8e minicomputer racks (1971)

***Focus*:** Looking at the author's technology path.

Let's take a look at some of the technology used.

I had one of these computers for many years.

I will include some fun chapters on my technology history, to provide some diversion and let your mind rest between the heavier stuff.

This is some of the technology I have experienced over 67 years. I have been around for quite a while now, involved in biomedical, environmental, diving, military, police, security, medical, industrial, automotive, transport, marine, agricultural, robotics, vision, automation and research systems.

My main focus since the 60s has largely been on building customised hardware and software as computerised instrumentation systems, used in calibration, measurement, logging, controlling, analysis and reporting. This has included fabrication, site installation, commissioning and support.

This work often involved designing and building many types of industrial computers, embedded computers and interface subsections for Serial, PC Bus and TCP interface systems, including analog IO, digital and timer I/O signals, linking to all sorts of sensors, gauges, devices, cameras, servos, hydraulics, VSDs, Pumps, PLCs, PACs, embedded micros and others.

XB102 PNP transistor, early 1950s

This does not mean, of course, that I am good at all of this work; it just means I have been there and played around in the technologies and made things work, eventually. I seem to be getting better at this endeavour, after all of these years (lol). Maybe I am a slow learner, but that is okay.

I remember as a child of five or six working with my brother building crystal sets. A diode was a little piece of coke or crystal, scratched with a fine silver wire (yes!) or a germanium diode and even a Ferranti/Ediswan XB102 PNP point contact geranium AF transistor driving the earphones. Yes, it was like a little flower; actually, it looked like this little black top hat. This was just a year or two after PNP point contact transistors were commercially available. That black top hat was glass and if you scratched the paint off, the transistor was light sensitive, as we discovered — a bit of a head scratch when you are a child. Turn your bed light on and the radio stops?

We then progressed to miniature tubes like 1T4 and 1S4 because they were low cost and used 1.5 VDC filaments (D cells). We had batteries for the B+ lines of 45/90 VDC (Leclanché stacks), although these tubes would run on 9 VDC on the plate quite well. We learned to solder and read resistor and capacitor codes.

We wound AM and SW copper wire coils on empty toilet cardboard rolls (shellacked in place), made RF re-gen circuits with audio reflex feedback, strung up very long horizontal antennas with insulators at each end, made copper pipe grounds and then listened to the world.

Just to give some idea of how quiet the radio space was back then, very occasionally at night, I could listen to San Fran and LA AM radio from New Zealand. The Australian eastern and western AM (2000 to 5000 km away) were usually easier to receive, though not always. All with one RF transistor or a mini tube with RF re-gen & audio reflex, a good antenna and copper rod for the earth plus high-impedance headphones. I also listened to short-wave hams, Voice of America, BBC, and Radio Luxembourg etc.

1S4 mini tube, mid 1950s

By the time I was 12, I could fix most radios, the superheterodynes, but also old, very old ones, back to handmade tube radios, with multi-staged tuned RF circuits. Beautiful things.

I had no idea I was playing with ground-breaking technology of the World War I era.

Then I progressed to repairing friends' TVs, which were tricker and more dangerous, as they had very high voltage on those CRTs. I didn't have a scope.

The way I learnt about all of this was to read technical books, then look up the words I didn't know and then re-read the text until I understood; well, sort of. Self-taught is always best; it's slower but provides a greater depth.

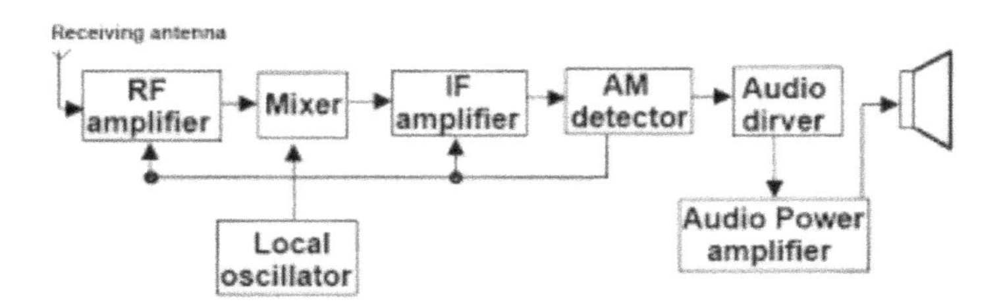

Block diagram of a Superheterodyne AM Receiver

During my early teenage years, I started reading about Tesla and Armstrong and other great minds, and I progressed to building test gear, multimeters, oscillators as generators, and high VDC power supplies.

By the time I was 16, I could build in all the technology available to me. I knew logic but had no idea about computing systems. Even a slide rule was foreign. I had a reasonable knowledge of electrical and electronic theory, tubes, transistors, mechanics, and maths such as calculus. There were no electronic calculators in my world.

Slide rule

Eventually, I ended up leaving New Zealand to go to the British Columbia Institute of Technology (BCIT), in Canada, to study biomedical electronics. It was there that I ran into a retired US air force colonel who had been part of the design team for the first US military digital computers made in the 1940s and early 50s. He had set up at BCIT and had a lab full of Raytheon military trainer gear and DEC PDP 8 computers. Was I lucky or what! He knew almost everything and tried to teach us that. We built all the digital computer sub-assemblies directly in the Raytheon trainers.

In that period, DEC was developing and selling low-cost digital minicomputers: a 4K Core RAM PDP 8I or 8L cost about $US18,000 to $25,000, and later in 1970 the 4K TTL PDP 8e with a Teletype was about $6000 to $7000.

PDP 8 internal view (1968)

To build DAQ instrumentation before these digital computers, we only had analog devices such as light and ink oscillograph paper recorders, with amps and filters, servo paper recorders, x-y paper recorders, analog FM–FM tape recorders, scopes, generators, 4–20mA loop instruments, set-point controllers and the best of all the toys for me, programmable analog computers which were limited but a heap of fun to play with. We built a lot of the analog stuff. Quite a lot of this stuff was even tube technology.

When I say program an analog computer, it really means configure the data (voltage levels), driving waveform shape generators, the clocks and timers, the interconnection of the maths blocks, differential amps configured to be adders, subtracters, log, differentiators, integrators, comparators etc. usually capacitors and resistors setups and other parameters, to create the solution or result, which usually came out on a storage oscilloscope or an x-y recorder as a mathematical plot.

There was no text output but instead, a dynamic generated voltage by the maths computing circuits which would run a computation series through and then reset and run again. You could adjust the maths parameters while it ran, allowing the user real-time interaction.

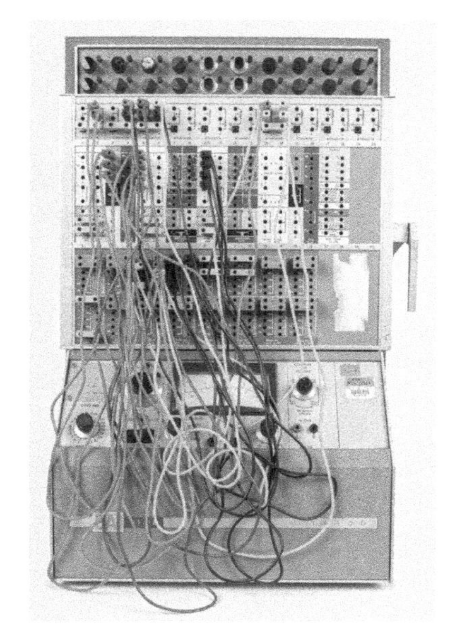

An analogue computer (1950s)

The program running was not code but maths running inside a time envelope, voltage over time, manipulated by the maths blocks.

There are all sorts of analog circuits for doing general maths and calculus. All this technology was born in the 1930s and 40s with the development of the first tube operational amplifiers. Thankfully, the dual triode was developed, which allowed the first differential amplifiers to be made. By the late 1950s, analog computers were hugely popular and used in all research institutions. At that date. they had become silicon transistor based and some were even starting to use the early hybrid integrated circuits. The big companies manufacturing then were EIA and Philbrick Nexus in the USA. Excellent and absolutely amazing high quality products.

Doing calculus was a dream come true on an analog computer, the metaphor was more apt than for a digital computer. You could play calculus with your fingertips on a potentiometer dial or two.

Analog computing was dying away when I came on to it, so I was only exposed for a short time. It was getting replaced with hybrid computers, a mix of analog computing and digital computing. The digital computers then were often too slow to do some of the maths, and often analog circuits were used to do that. Hybrid computers disappeared rapidly once digital computers' clocking rates, memory and computational power increased in the 60s. Having Fortran and Basic helped a lot, as now we could express ideas in the written and spoken language, not mnemonics, binary, octal or hex.

For me, the analog computing lessons stuck and I continue to love analog circuitry, using op amps and instrumentation grade amps. I, like many others, had many Fairchild 709 op amps turn red hot when they broke into uncontrollable feedback. (Burnt fingertips.)The 741 was the saviour of the times. National Semi went on to become the standard for most analog chips.

One early project I was given in which to try out my analog computing knowledge was to develop an analog biomedical instrument that would take a blood pressure waveform and capture and hold the systolic and diastolic pressures and display this data on two small seven-segment LED displays. To connect and use this new blood pressure display instrument was easy: connect it directly to a calibrated analog output of a blood pressure monitor (usually with a CRT display) and there on the two LED digit displays were the two pressures. This new instrument was very helpful in both operating and recovery rooms, as the two numbers told staff what they needed to know.

I also had access to all types of electronic, chemical and medical measurement and analysis instruments, chromatography, spectrophotometers, mass spectrometers, pH meters, CO_2, N_2, O_2 gas analysers, temperature RTDs and TCs, EKGs, EEGs, EMGs, plethysmograph, scopes, storage scopes, generators, precision power supplies and more. There was a lot of technology. My lab was always filled with these things, to work with and tools, tools and tools.

I also did prototyping using breadboarding and I managed PCB making, double-sided. I used coloured tape to lay these out on Mylar to make masks, all hand done.

I just kept moving with the times, using what came along that was helpful.

Digital computers consumed most of my time with interfacing and programming.

Calibration of instruments became an obsession.

Let's return to LabVIEW again.

CHAPTER 3
HIDDEN DATA: REMOVING CONSTANTS

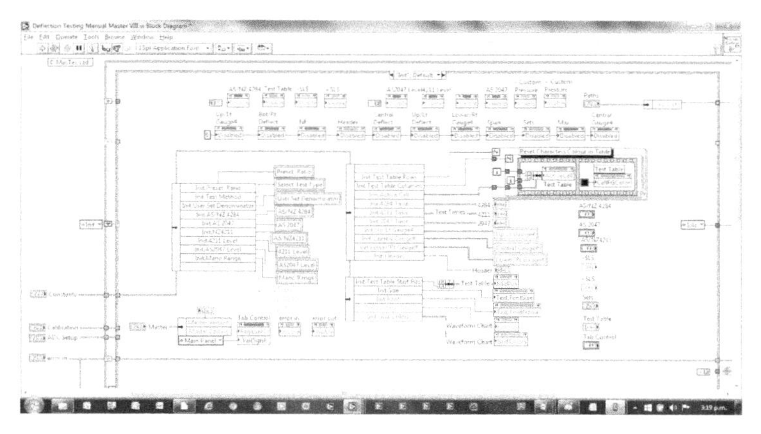

LCOD Hidden data: Removing all constants from LabVIEW diagrams to a disk file; and loading them back into the diagram from the disk file at run time

Focus: “Hidden Data” or “Removing Constants from LabVIEW programs”.

WHY I DEVELOPED THIS NEW LCOD HIDDEN DATA METHOD

A Software Engineering Approach to LabVIEW is an important, groundbreaking book. It is very “English” in manner: funny, challenging and cryptic and splendid. It takes a bit of reading back and forth to get its message and to understand. I read the book around 2004.

It was quite a few years later, during some upgrade work on an old piece of software, that I started to deliberately include some of the ideas from that book. I was certainly not as thorough or rigorous as the authors, but I did enjoy what they advocated. It got me going. It increased my awareness.

However, when I came to the part in the book on “hidden data — removing constants from LV diagrams”, I struggled with what was said using “ini files” and even the examples were difficult. It seemed to me to be a non-LabVIEW solution. It seemed to be a method lifted from code work.

I fought around the edges of this “ini files” “hidden data — removing constants” for quite some time after that, even upgrading and improving what was in the book, and eventually I gave up and sat back for a year or two, to let the ideas settle.

Several advanced programmers have mentioned “hidden data” methods in books and blogs over the years and offered part solutions, but they have always been complex and have not really solved the base issues. I just figured, all those authors knew more about this than me, so just do what they say, but I couldn't. The methods were too limiting and not at all LabVIEW centric.

What I wanted to be able to achieve, was to remove out of the diagrams to disk “All constants and that included all LabVIEW's Graphical Constants”, that is LEDs, switches, rings, enums, clusters, math formulas, paths, VISA, ActiveX, and IP, and bring it all back into the diagrams from disk with “No loss of graphical nature”.

LabVIEW is graphical, not code work.

Then, at some point, I realised that I already had the method to remove all these types of graphical and other constants, and you may use the exact same method. I have been using parts of this hidden data method, which I am about to show you, since LabVIEW 1.0 beta, and I just did not realise, until a few years back, that it was the basis of a method to expand on how to "remove constants" from programs in a clearer, more formulated, rigorous way and keep the "graphical nature". I had been using this same method, in a little less refined way, for all the time I had been programming in LV.

This book is certainly not the final say on this matter, I'm sure. So please expand this or butcher it up to make a better solution, if you get a sudden revelation of the next step.

Or

You may laugh and say what rubbish and nonsense; that is okay too.

By the way, I still have my Mac SE with LV 1 on it.

Obsessed sort of.

CHAPTER 4

TECHNOLOGY HISTORY 2

DEC's famous DEC tape system

Focus: Looking at the author's technology path.

I started learning how to use DEC PDP 8 digital computers to develop programmed instrumentation solutions. I first used a 1967 PDP 8I (DTL) computer and the slower 1967 PDP 8Ss (12-bit serial), and later the 1970 PDP 8e (TTL).

The first few programmed solutions were 12 bit binary or machine coded. I had to paddle (front panels switches were called paddles) 12 bit binary machine codes and data into the machine to program them. As I progressed, I moved on to punched paper tape programs prepared on a teletype that were written in ASCII text as assembler. When I had more memory and DEC tapes, I progressed to SABR Assembler with Fortran II plus the rapid build Focal. Memory cost around $US3000 to $5000 for 4 K of either magnetic core or the new dynamic silicon RAM (12 bit words) in about 1972.

ASR33 Teletype

The DEC minicomputer's "user interface" was usually an ASR33 Teletype. A Teletype was a heavy clunky thing driven by an electric motor, with gears and clutches. It made a lot of noise. It had a keyboard, an ink character printer, a paper tape punch and paper tape reader (10 char/sec). These were connected to DEC computers using a 4-20mA current loop RS-232 interface running at 110 baud or 10 char/sec.

Later, DEC Writers were used and if you were rich a Beehive ASCII CRT Terminal or even the IBM Selectric golf ball typewriter (15 char/sec).

DECwriter terminal (1972)

By this time, I had moved into research at Simon Fraser University in British Columbia, and my job was building biomedical research multi-variable instrumentation systems, which you could not buy but were needed.

I made the decision in 1970 that a digital computer was always going to be the basis of every new complex instrument system I built. The reason, of course, was that software was king and allowed a soft solution, rather than a hardware-only solution. Hence the name soft-ware, i.e. spongy.

It suited me, as you could iterate around with soft codes to get the programmable adjustable instrument hardware running correctly. It also allowed code to sort out the simple design problems.

Also printing summary and combined analytical results was so much better than paper off multiple x-y plotter graphs or strip charts that then needed hours of ruler and calculator time to make a summary or report of all the data translated into numbers.

It was a revolution to be able to craft software to do this. I was playing with magic.

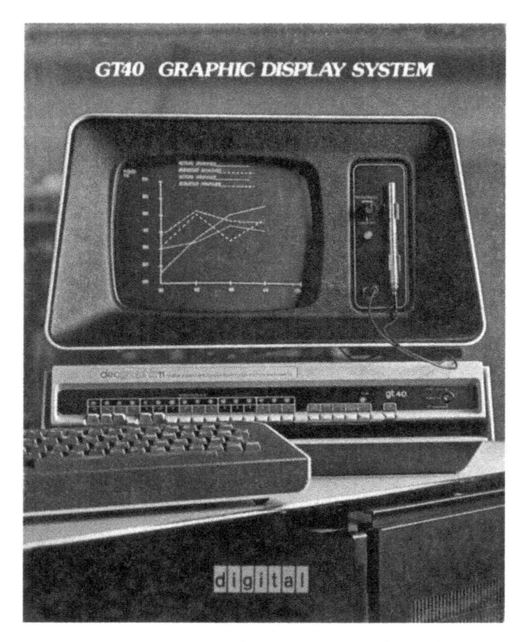

DEC GT40 Graphics Computer (1973)

It must be explained that the instruments being built were not single instruments but a fusing together of many analog instruments with a computer sitting in the middle, interfaced to them, acquiring data and controlling I/O, calculating and then making printed results or displaying results on other devices.

At that time, I called them multi-variable instrumentation. This was really the beginning of my virtual instrumentation techniques. The software was the solution and virtualised or was the metaphor of the whole instrument.

I did not have a DEC CRT display until 1973 when a DEC GT-40 computer was purchased which had a vector display (not a pixel display). The GT-40 had a PDP 11-05 plus on top of a vector display computer: two computers in one box.

Before the DEC GT-40 arrived, to display data, I would drive an HP storage scope's x-y-z inputs with the PDP 8's two-channel DAC plus the beam control z axis digital output interface that I built. A very simple vector generator.

This HP Scope display combo was a massive revolution too. Seeing the data as a graph on the screen was another huge jump. It would happen in Real Time.

That DEC GT-40 was used to create dancing stick figures with the Laban Code, a choreographer's method of writing "time and 3D space movement of human limbs". This work later progressed to more powerful SUN workstations when bodies were added to the stick figures. It was the beginning of animation. The SUN Mini could make the filled-out figures dance ballet very very slowly.

The custom ADC, DAC, Digital I/O and Timer interfaces were built and interfaced to the DEC minicomputers and then the software developed in Assembler, Focal or Fortran and even Dartmouth Basic. Thus, the new multi-variable instrument was slowly birthed, with much tweaking, debugging and optimising.

Buying hardware like ADC and DAC sub-assemblies was very expensive and also limiting. I used to build all my own external interfaces and directly wire them into the computer's backplane. It was all wire-wrapped boards and ribbon cables, not soldered. These devices were not interfaced to I/O ports but they all became part of the computer's backplane.

I had the source code for the DEC PDP 8 Focal and I added my own commands sets to the Focal interpreter code to extend its usefulness, with Fcore and Fexe etc. Being able to jump to Assembler was a big help with the low-level stuff.

I worked alone, as there was no one else around that knew this technology. I was 20 years old when I started and thought it all quite normal, not even thinking about the fact that no other generation had ever seen this stuff before.

I must mention some other old technologies from back then (this will make you laugh).

The university department I worked in had many mechanical Singer calculators that I fixed. I did not really know how they worked, but I always got them going again when they got stuck or locked up. A hammer and a small punch sorted them. Sewing machine oil was useful also.

It was during this early period of building research instrumentation that I started realising how important calibration was to assuring good and meaningful results from these types of complex multi-variable instruments. It wasn't just a matter of using so-called calibrated instruments; it was understanding system-level calibration at the physics and chemical level. Many faulty assumptions on calibration were and are still being made.

During all this early instrumentation and calibration work, I released a technical paper on the subject of calibration methods for exercise physiology VO_2 gas systems. This paper showed much or most previous historical work could be faulty due to insufficient understanding of gas laws and water vapour measurement, leading to faulty calibration of gas-measuring instruments.

Note: it was the analysis of the printed data from the DEC computers that gave me the clues for the need to publish a paper. Something was often wrong with the VO2 test results and it wasn't clear what. I could not get consistency. Everyone just trusted the results; it was a bizarre time.

The calibration methods I developed and used were direct instrument calibration, with calibration data being stored right into the computer memory while the sensors were reading known controlled calibration standards.

We used Scholander chemical gas analysers to derive the CO_2, O_2 and N_2 calibration gas concentration standards. Two operators would sit back to back and drive the Scholanders and then they would compare results. This work would continue until the results were consistent and close to one another by +/- 0.01% or so.

The CO_2 concentration was about 0.034% in 1970 at our mountaintop labs.

So I started using “direct calibration”. I never trusted instruments’ calibration certificates unless there was a primary or a certified secondary calibration standard available to verify it.

Using my new method, all the calibration data was remade each time for a test and stored directly in the software every time the test program ran.

ABOUT THE BIG DILEMMA: PROGRAMMING INSTRUMENTATION SOLUTIONS

Instrumentation programmers are always forced to become very familiar with the details for which they are going to build systems. If you are going to program these advanced solutions, you cannot fudge it, as you will get caught out very quickly, with calibration errors and the like.

This is still often the most limiting area of hiring a programmer to write instrumentation software. Do they know the subject being programmed thoroughly, or are you going to have to teach them all you know, to get the results you want?

What we needed was a better programming system that allowed engineers to become programmers, then that loop of teaching programmers would go. The question then arises, of course, of whether engineers can become good programmers. From experience I think that sometimes they can, but most times they cannot. Instrumentation programming is a complex, exacting business and only a few are capable of working in that environment.

Dozens of real-time measurement and control instruments were developed during this period at the university, using DEC and other computers and technologies, and all types of research was carried out.

Multi-variable instruments were built for many disciplines over a 17-year period, covering environmental, diving, exercise physiology, motor learning, biomechanics, biochemistry, neurophysiology, kin anthropometry and others.

It should also be noted that, until about 1967, there were no OSs for small minicomputers. Minis were raw beasts, without even a boot ROM. The ROM, EPROM or EEPROM had not been invented, and neither had Dynamic or Static Silicon RAM.

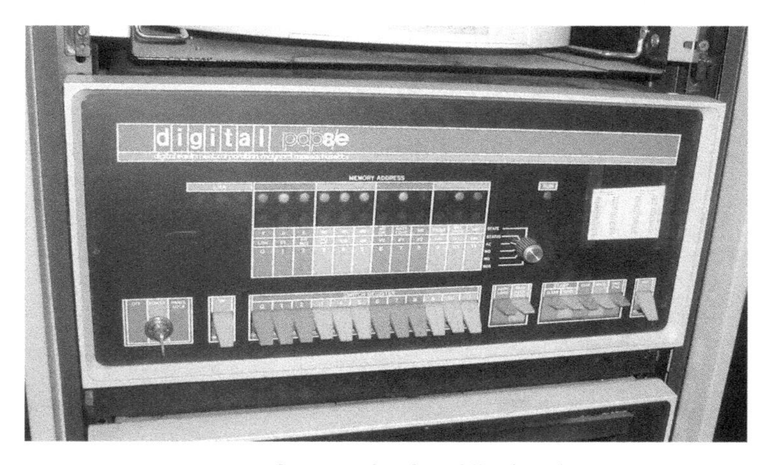

PDP8e front panel with paddles (1971)

You actually had to hand load a bootstrap code block manually into the core memory (magnetic memory) to make them do anything. The bootstrap loader usually only started a paper tape reader to read in the next level binary loader until you could do something useful. However, when you had loaded your program code and hit the run button, you had the full machine, nothing else was in the way, so real time was real time. Maths was slow but I/O was fast. DMA ran the tape or disk systems, interrupts were used to clock the instruments program, run the DAQ and make everything tight and synced. Instrumentation solutions were not OS spongy back then, like they often are now.

The first OS I used was DEC's PS-8, leading to OS-8, and what a revelation, using DEC tapes, not disks, as the storage devices. DEC 32 K disks were

$US10,000, so instead I used DEC tapes with 384 K Words. The OS-8 allowed edited Fortran text code to be stored and then compiled on the DEC tape system, or you could write up some Focal Interpreter code and run off the tape. It was quite something to see the little DEC tapes whizz around and rock back and forth doing their thing and then, clunk, the teletype would print the results of the compilation.

Twin DECtape system (1968)

As a historical note: The DOS that Microsoft put out in the early 80s for the IBM PC was modelled off CPM which in tun was modelled off these DEC operating systems. The single cmd line: in Microsoft OSs today follows CPM and this original DEC OS work.

While building multi-variable multi-device instrumentation systems, there were other technology areas that had to be developed to work with the digital computer analog and digital interfaces. These included building or buying devices such as multi-channel EEGs, EMGs, EKGs, metabolic and respiratory electronic instruments plus a host of sensors and other home made gear. Most of this technology was analog, with instrumentation-grade amps, and active filters.

Then there was the digital I/O, usually built from TTL 74LS or CMOS 4000 series and later OPTO 22's optically isolated SSRs for AC and DC power systems.

This really made the End Solutions a hybrid computing system that was quite complex because of the biomedical nature and safety requirements. Yes, we were concerned about leakage currents back then. Everything was leakage tested and certified with stickers, like now.

Over the 1970s and 80s, the research instrument development work progressed to include more interface methods, HPIB/GPIB, higher speed serial baud rates and more accurate DAQ systems.

HP RTE100 minicomputer (1981)

New minicomputers started to appear, Varians, HP 2114/6s, PDP11, LSI 11s (ours had a 5 Meg 12-inch removable platter disk - awesome) and later the HP RTE 1000 (1 MIPS) machines, almost Unix, with up to 12–25 users at a time. The 70 MB HPIB disk drive was $US75,000. All the users connected to the computer could be running analysis programs, collecting data on the ADC and other IO plus developing programs and compiling all at the same time. There was no graphical display to soak up the CPU; it was all Serial ASCII Terminals. Impressive computer.

As early as 1970, I built a Real Time VO_2 data capture and analysis instrument using a PDP 8e with ADC and DAC, plus a Westinghouse (zirconium fuel cell) O_2 meter and Capnograph (Infrared) CO_2 Gas analyser, EKG heart rate meter, flow/volume meter, and temperature probes to collect respiratory data off athletes and cardiac research subjects. It may have been the first real-time VO_2 system in the world, beating NASA.

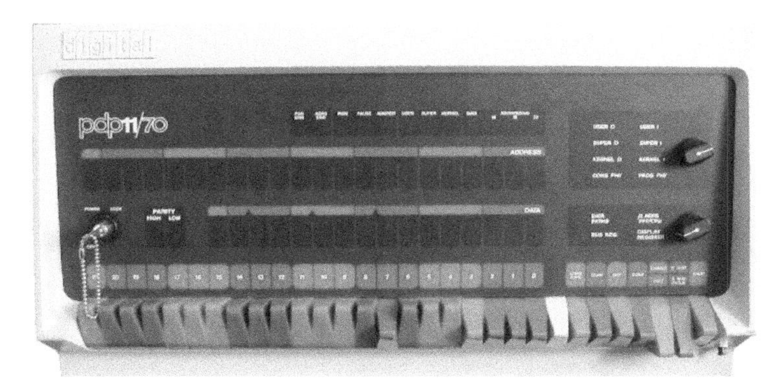

DEC 11 front panel with paddles (1979)

With that VO2 instrument, we could rapidly test large quantities of subjects. There were none of the old methods, no gas bags, no glass gas sample syringes, no Haldane or Scholander chemical gas analysers, no calculator or hand paperwork. The computer results printed out on the Teletype directly as the subjects exercised. The Russians sent their National / Army ice hockey teams, the Americans their professional football teams, the Canadians their Olympic skaters, athletes and teams of all sorts. We tested many Olympic and endurance athletes on this system over the years.

In 1972 we even had early HP computers with HPIB (the first name for GPIB). These were medical measurement systems. This new HPIB bus and expandable daisy chain cable system was a revolution for building many biomedical test systems. The ability to mix many single-function instruments on an addressable bus allowed multi-variable instruments to be created with a computer doing the linking and collection plus analysis and display. The computer looked like a glorified calculator running an early form of HP Basic.

Big statistical computation was always done on the IBM 360 and 370 mainframe computers, using punched cards and doing batch processing. It was manual punching of cards also. We had no way of sending ASCII data to an IBM punch-card machine that used EBCDIC codes.

This required teams of people doing this typing work and they were very fast. It was nothing to have hundreds, sometimes thousands, of punch cards to load into the IBMs.

Amazing stuff.

That's all we had, but we didn't know otherwise.

We were having fun.

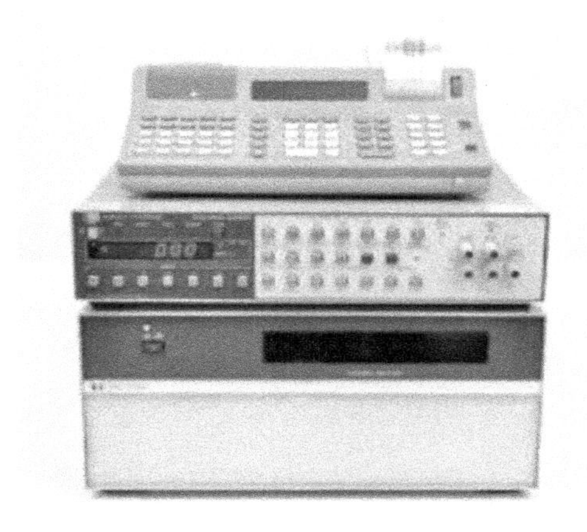

Early HPIB instruments and computer

CHAPTER 5
THE QUESTIONS I ASKED

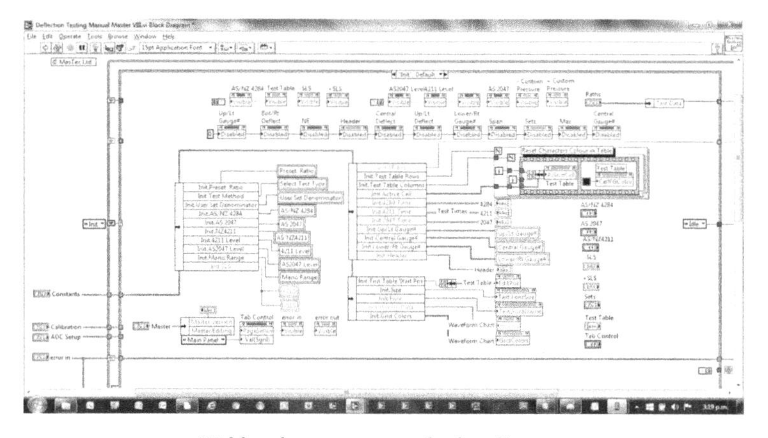

Hidden data recover method to diagram

***LCOD Focus*:** Hidden Data.

THE FIVE QUESTIONS I ASKED

Now, let's get started on achieving LabVIEW "hidden data".

The questions that I posed to myself to start the Hidden data evolution process were:

1. How can we remove *all and any types* of LabVIEW constants out of the diagram?
2. How can we remove those constants out of the program to file in a disk storage system?
3. How can we recover those constants from the file storage system back into the diagram?
4. How can we reinstall the constants into the diagram at load or run time or any time?
5. How can we make an online and offline editor to edit all those removed constants?

So there are several tasks to do.

As an encouragement, when you get to the end of this little evolutionary story, you will have all of these posed questions answered and more.

I will show a simple system to remove and store constants in files, plus a read/write system to allow editing of those files.

At run time, those files are read and the constant reappears in the diagram to be used. Just what we want!

Actually of course, only the constant's data comes back, not the actual original constant graphic.

I have written this book for beginners, with loads of LV screen shots. I am assuming experienced programmers will look quickly over the pages with the pics and get it within a few minutes.

This "New Improved Removing constants" or "hidden data" method only takes a little extra work. You can take diagrams full of constants, as the next few pages will show, and remove constants rapidly.

The method allows the use of "all and any type of LabVIEW constant" (most important), in any quantity and that includes all those lovely LV Graphical

Constants rather than just simple arrays, text, numerics or booleans to be removed and hidden and then recalled.

A general point about my own LV programming style: It is very easy and convenient to drop constants everywhere in the diagrams, so as to get the job done. "Oh, I need to select DAQ Ch 6 here, pop a Graphical enum Constant out of the DAQ driver Icon terminal and there is the Graphical Constant." However, the constants need to be removed from the diagram to make it clean and be adjustable off line also. All constants are moved "out of the diagram" into a storage device, to be read back at run time.

Even now my method for LabVIEW development style still involves the traditional convenient LabVIEW way of dropping constants on the diagram. Yes, I do, just to get it all going quickly. Then I add at the end of that development work a very easy clean-up technique for the "removing of constants", which then translates them into something much more useable.

This method is not new, as we have all been doing parts of this method from the beginning of LV. However, this is a focused process to convert programs into having hidden data constants stored in files with recall to the diagram plus off-line editing.

I use this method for far more than just number, boolean, and string constants. It can be used for any special constant data, Paths, DAQ, GPIB, Serial, math formulas, VISA, IVI, Active X and most importantly, Graphical Rings and enums.

SOME BACKGROUND ON HOW THIS "HIDDEN DATA" METHOD EVOLVED

My first real LabVIEW program I built in mid-1987 ran on a Mac II with a 21-inch white screen, very impressive and slick for the time, as no one had 21-inch white screens except SUN people.

For DAQ, I used the new NI NB-GPIB connected to a HP 3497 6.5-digit DVM + 32-channel mux.

While developing this program, I used constants through the diagrams, as you do, but quickly found as a LV rookie that when I came to run and debug my work, it was not possible to change the program on the fly because of all those embedded diagram constants.

So in ignorant desperation, I fudged a solution: I made the constants into controls (variables) and hid them to the side of the main user front panel, so I could scroll sideways and adjust them while the program was running and see if the new constant value would fix what was going wrong. Sounds like a variable to me, you will say. *No, it is a constant that needs its value defined.*

"Program playing" requires this sometimes and when you are finished doodling, you can hide the controls off to the side, by popping off the terminal and selecting "Hide control". I bet you have used this method also, at some time. Maybe you have put the maths constants, GPIB or DAQ config details off to the side of the actual displayed front panel.

As this method developed, I added clusters in which to embed the constant (adjustable), so I could unbundle them all off one wire, back into the diagram. In LV1, there was no "Unbundle by name".

Yes, the method starts evolving, getting clearer and cleaner even before the end of 1988. As I progressed this method, my front panels started to include these "Clusters of Undetermined constants" in my programming work, hidden off to the side (hidden data, sort of LOL). This was 15 years before I read *A Software Engineering Approach to LabVIEW*. The book's discussion on hidden data just spurred me on to find a better LV way to do hidden data.

I worked on and off for several years before I finally realised I was already doing it. I just needed to complete to the obvious end point, and finish the list of my five questions.

My program front panels started to look like this next pic. The blue parameter cluster (or COC) is not normally seen by the operator, but the programmer knows that it is there. Not really a good method but simple and often used.

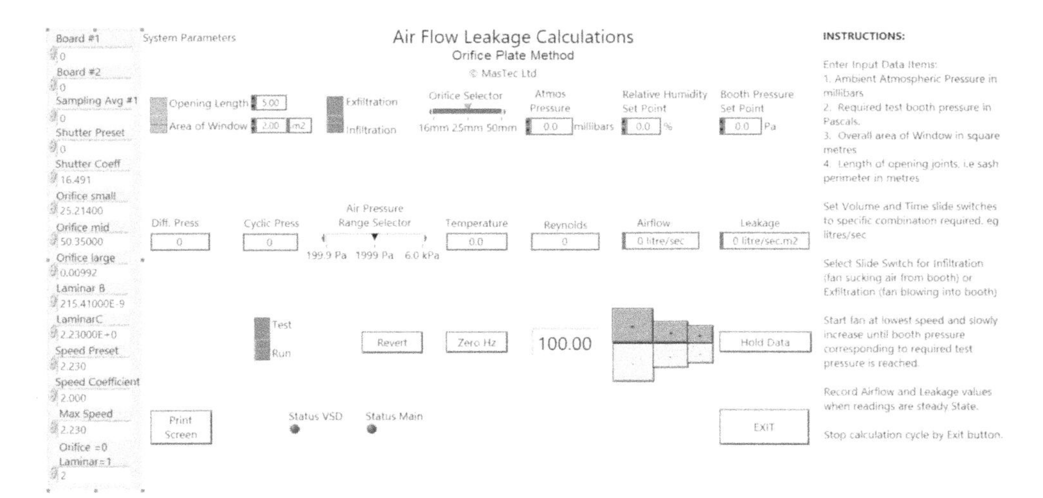

The beginnings of COCs

I used this original COC in an industrial test project for a large washing machine maker in the USA. I was building a "washing machine drum destruction testing machine". My LabVIEW controlled it all, with that blue COC idea brewing away.

After the debug and commission, I could hide the COC with one-click pop and select "Hide COC". When I was lazy, I also sometimes just embedded the COC or COCs in the user front panel, so I could adjust them, without the scroll sideways. They in fact become "Permanent Adjustable Constants". But this made the front panel too complex and busy.

What do all those extra controls actual do? Yes, they provide confusion for the operator! Also the operator may change them, oops.

Luckily for us all, LabVIEW also had a selection under the Operate Menu so that you could store all the front panel present control values as default values. This meant you could get back all those old constant values in the COC when you reloaded the VI or selected "Restore Default".

A lot of programmers still use this method, but they are not really aware they are removing constants from diagrams in those semi-variable controls. It is a little dangerous also, if you forget to make them default values. All that hard work of commissioning the values can be lost.

I continued using this method for some time and my front panels always had secret variables (a COC or several COCs) hidden off to the side, so the operators could not see them but I could recall them when I was developing, debugging and commissioning. Messy but practical for me and I had no reason yet to make a better mouse trap.

Another technique that I tried was to make a front panel button pop up a small panel that exposes a "COC" that are adjusted and then the panel is closed. This is useful for loop tuning, PID coefficients and the like.

Tab Control

When the "Tab Control" was added to LV, I think about LV 5/6, I started using this to put the "COC" in additional Front Panel Tabs. This Tab framework made things tidier and ordered and now the COCs are not hidden off to the side or have the need for scrolling to be hidden away from the main user front panel.

I sometimes made the COC sit on a front panel of a SubVI. I could pop this type of front panel up with a button and adjust things and then re-save it. parameter setting, I called it. The next pic displays this. It is a primitive COC Editor.

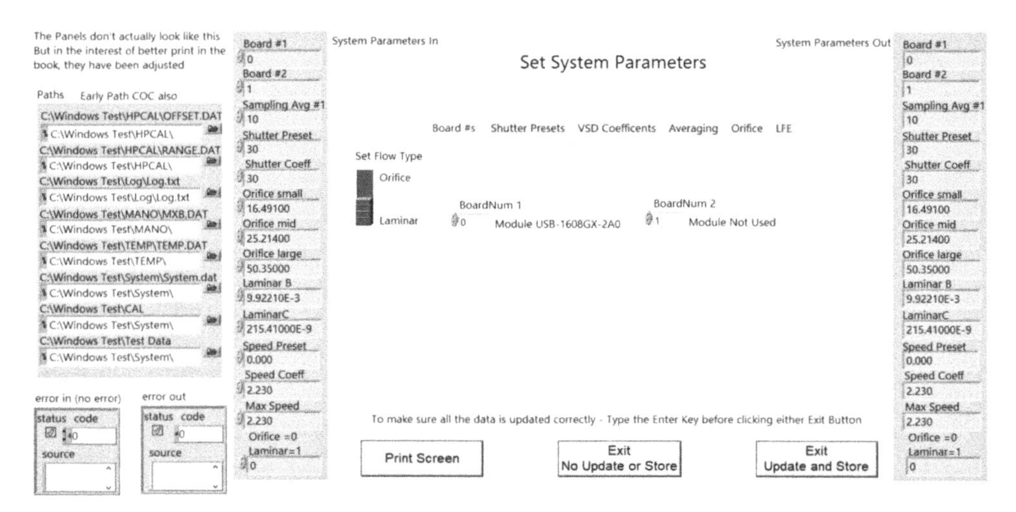

Continued COC evolution with tabs

The Tab Control shows the name of the constants hidden/stored inside the Tab:

- Tab Board #s has DAQ info
- Tab Shutter has shutter/servo system info
- Tab VSD has motor info
- Tab Averaging has DAQ adjustment for noise
- Tab Orifice and Tab Laminar are fixed calibration terms.

A beginning. This front panel shows an early form of an Editor for constants inside Tabs. Later I will show the diagram for this early simple Editor. Then further into this discussion, the newer LCOD Editor will be shown.

An editor is required to allow adjusting the COC values stored on disk files when commissioning, debugging and support.

This editing of COCs can also be done offline or off-site. Use Team-viewer to remotely edit the hidden data COC files and then re-save back to the disk on the remote LV program. If you do this, the next run time the new stored hidden data COCs will be loaded and the fix is made.

Main Front Panel and COCs in a series of Tabs

The next evolution is shown in the next pic: Tabs again.

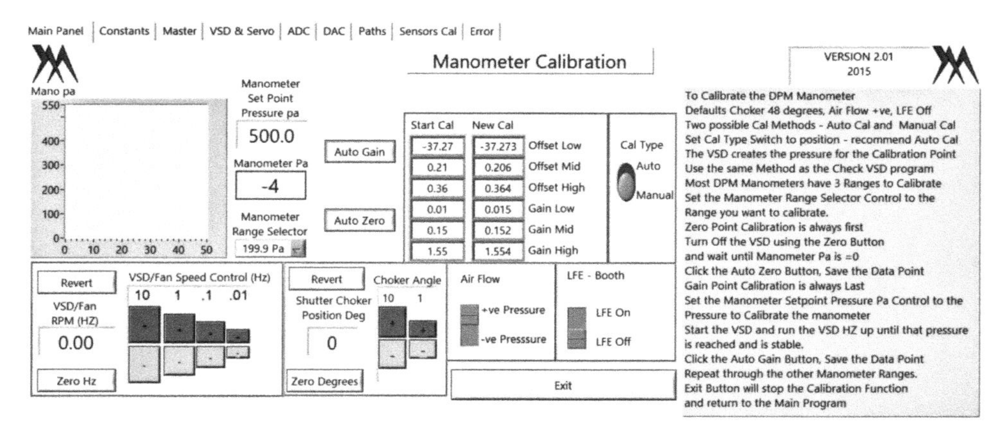

COC expansion into front panel tabs

The main front panel and all the COCs are placed in a series of Tabs.

1. COC are now put in an orderly place.
2. These COC Tabs can be hidden at run time with the property Page Selector visible Tab
3. Then the main front panel only will be visible, just like a normal SubVI.
4. The COC Tabs have public data as controls and private data as indicators.
5. This evolution now includes SubVIs front panels also.

I also made a set of Tab names and placement rules for the main VI and all SubVIs.

The first Tab position = Main Operator Panel, is always the main application's front panel or in the case of SubVI's its main front panel.

This first Tab is to allow the operator to control the program as it runs.

The next series of Tabs are for public data COCs = Master, VSD, ADC, DAC, Paths, Cal, Messages etc. (more can be added as needed).

It is starting to look more orderly, and who knows what is behind those Tabs? Only the programmer knows.

Loading and Saving Hidden Data to file

After this evolution, the next step in the puzzle to solve was:

“How to save the hidden data as Tabs of (COCs) to a file for safekeeping and at run time loading and recovery of the COC data on file back into the diagram”.

Also, the editor would still need to be made to provide online and offline edit ability of COCs.

As mentioned, the above Front Panel Tabs Master, VSD, ADC, DAC, Paths etc. are public data COCs. These COC’s data are available to all the SubVIs.

The only exception to this in the Tab group we skipped over and that is the Tab “constants” which is used to display the private data in the COC for the particular SubVI.

Note: The private data COC is only loaded inside this SubVI. That is why the private data COC is an indicator not a control. This means the private data COC is only ever inside this SubVI. The private data COC is never put on to SubVI’s terminals and allowed to escape. No coupling allowed.

The last Tab, “Sensors Cal”, is a public data COC and is loaded from disk from the calibration files area.

- Public COCs: the whole program can see these COCs. The multiple public data COCs usually reside on the Main Program’s State Engine outside loop on individual shift registers.

- Private COCs: these are only ever inside SubVIs and no other part of the program knows about them or ever sees them. This is private data for that particular SubVI. Again, establishing "*No data coupling*".

The Public Data COCs are connected to the SubVI's terminals.

Notice I broke up the COCs into functional groupings: Paths, Master, ADC, DIO, DAC, VSD, Servos. At run time the file loaded COCs are crafted back into the exact original saved COC.

When I am loading these main public COCs, I do it in several initialisation states and then the individual COC is wired to a separate shift register on the program's main while loop.

The shift registers keep the public data COC alive and available and the SubVIs can read and unbundle by name the public data COCs when and where they are required.

This pic below shows the Program's Outer Main State Engines Loop, with the first state being executed.

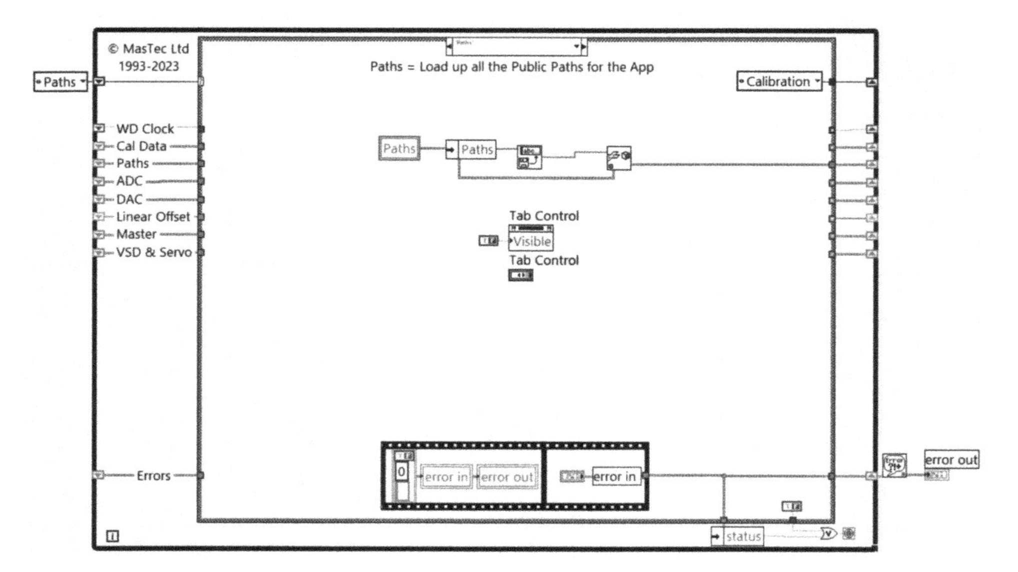

Recovering a paths COC from disk file

It is running the Initialisation State, called Paths, loading from disk the "Paths" COC.

Yes, this COC has "All the File Paths" used in the program.

So, that is the second time the method for loading and saving hidden data made as COCs is shown.

COC File Recovery

COCs are stored using the Flatten to String function and saved as encrypted binary files. No one can change them unless they have the key or shape of the COC in the file. The recovery is just the opposite. Use the Unflatten from String function as shown above.

Note: the key or shape of the COC file recovery is a local variable of the COC. This is not an accident or a mistake, but it is most helpful for later modification of the COC, when the COC internals expand or contract. Using a local variable for Type or Shape automatically updates type correctly for the unflatten process.

You can try this when you build your first hidden data program. Take any COC and add a new constant into it, save that COC and then reload it. Miraculously the COC is remade correctly, including the new constant, without you having to do anything.

The trick is the Local Variable giving the read for flatten string the new key or shape of the changed COC.

The program design evolved with diagrams like this pic below.

This Event structure sits in the Main Loops State Engine.

The event shown is for the "Static Pressure" Test SubVI.

When the front panel button "Test with Static Pressure" is clicked, this SubVI pops and runs with its front panel showing.

This SubVI has all public data inside it from the SRs wires connected to the SubVI's terminals.

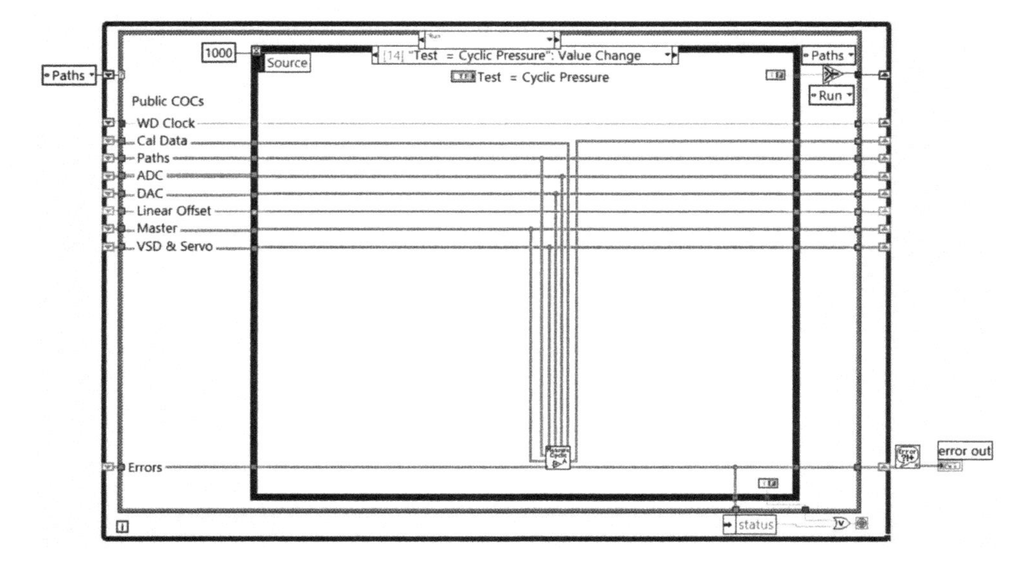

SRs holding public data COCs

My LCOD state engine diagrams always have a series of shift registers at the top of the loop which carry the public data COCs.

The only exception is the public COC error term SR which is always at the bottom of the loop.

This placement of the Error cluster placement arose from early LV1 instrument driver work.

In 1988 the COC error term in GPIB and serial instrument drivers was developed, and then later included in the early DAQ VIs.

This COC error term showed off data flow determinism very well. Before that error term addition you will find a lot of LV 1 programs using the sequence structure to create execution order.

Notice almost all the top level Test SubVIs carry the same Public Data COCs terminals and this starts to create uniformity in the program, with a structure and design that is easily learned and understood and repeated.

This next pic is from the same main program, but the event is SubVI "Calibrate Manometer".

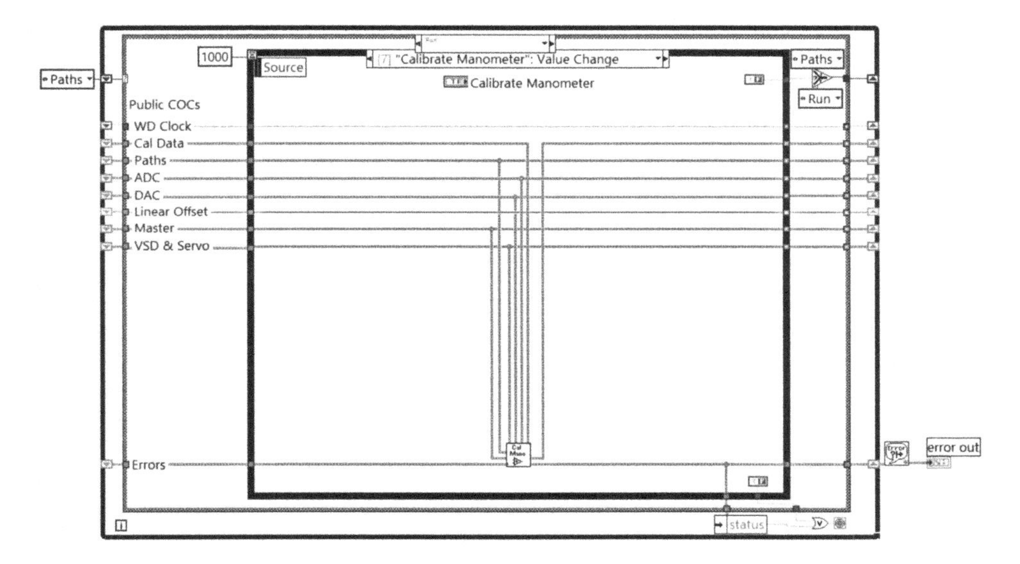

A calibration object that updates public data and file

The top SR called "Cal Data" in this SubVI is also a COC of data that contains all the calibration data. It is loaded at run time from disk also during the initialisation.

The "Cal Data" is public and the SubVI Calibrate Manometer uses this data whenever it runs, getting the Startup Cal data on to its Cal terminal. When the operator exits calibration of the manometer, the new Cal data comes out of the indicator Cal data indicator terminal updated and this is wired back to the main loop "Cal Data" SR (right) to update the data for the whole program.

All calibration sections work this way.

At any time during a test, the test can be stopped and calibration can be repeated. Sometimes a good idea if the test is long (all day) or the temperature changes over the test period etc.

Easy access to stored Cal Data and doing Re-calibration is most important.

I have actually seen and heard of Industrial Test Sites that never actual calibrate the test rig's sensors but instead rely on calibration lab certificates for their calibration data. Not a good idea.

Additionally, the new calibration data is written to the Cal data disk file inside the SubVI, using the Path COC to extract the correct path.

Note: that what is shown so far is just the main loop of a single-loop or single task program.

In most cases these Industrial Tester are multi-tasking and asynchronous. It is necessary to load all the public COCs outside all the multitasking State Engines and feed the COCs to each Task.

Here is some information on my early COC evolutionary steps:

- Storing COCs in files by converting the data in the COC to a spreadsheet file.
- Reload and read the spreadsheet file back, rebuild the COC by bundling into a cluster.

The next pic shows this old method. It is the beginnings of a type of COC editor's diagram. You can see it is clumsy compared to what flatten and unflatten can do so easily. Nasty.

Looking back at this initial early work, I realised in this method that all the data in the COCs were also just simple numeric, boolean, string or arrays, with *no* Graphical Constants (switches, rings, enums, paths, math formula, clusters, VISA, Active X etc.).

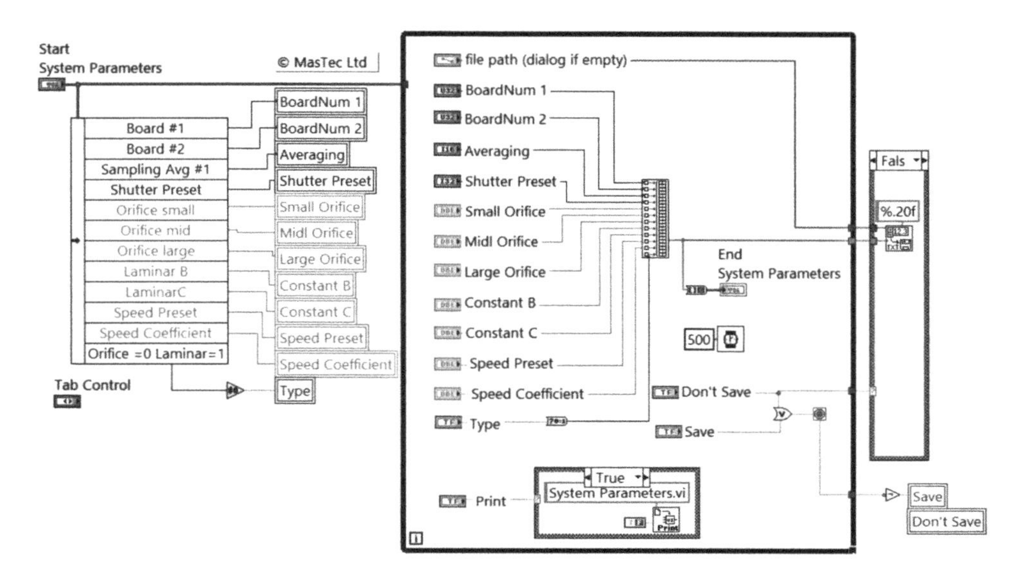

An early attempt to build hidden data files

It was some time after this work that I ran into the difficulty with the "Constant removal method" using the ini file system in the famous first LCOD book. This was a lightbulb moment and lead to the expansion and the solution of the new COC hidden data method.

What I started to realise was that I could clean up the "Constant removal method" and use it for removing both public and private data constants from the main application and also all the SubVIs.

I realised I needed to develop a more complete solution to handle these new thoughts.

I started to reflect on all those years of work wearing programmer's blinkers and not seeing a generalised outcome that would be helpful. I guess you only program what you know and need at the time.

As this new "hidden data" method developed, it became clearer that the "diagram look" started to benefit considerably as the work progressed. That is always a good hint that things are coming together. The diagrams became more unified, structured and readable, with more and more automatic documentation.

In all my development over the years, I preferred an evolutionary, iterative method of working and developing, probably because I am not clever enough to do the big bang method.

I admire people that can get the big idea and make it happen at once. Awesome.

For me, it takes time for the ideas to come out, be recognised, ordered and then put together.

I am basically a tinkerer type: try this, add this, change this and, hey, this looks promising.

Also to do it this way is a little more fun, rather than to just sit and formalise it all which I find is a little boring.

More soon.

CHAPTER 6
TECHNOLOGY HISTORY 3

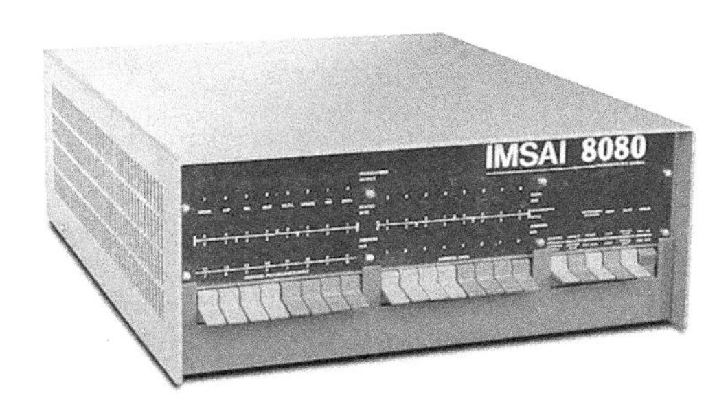

The famous IMSAI

Focus: A further look at the author's technology path.

My second-hand IMSAI S-100 system cost $US3000 in 1979 and came with both an 8080 CPU board and a Z80 CPU board, keyboard and CRT display, 64 KB RAM, EPROM Burner, DIO Card, and two 5.25-inch double-sided floppy 360K drives. It had installed CPM 2.2, Northstar Basic, an assembler, disassembler, spreadsheet and word processor. I added a dot matrix printer.

I also used this IMSAI in my 1802 and 8085 projects to burn my 2708/2716 EPROMs: just load the binary file and burn.

I made an EPROM eraser using a clothes dryer UV bulb in an empty coffee tin.

That would all cost about $US15,000+ in today's money, minus the coffee tin.

MICROS, NEW CHIPS, COMPLETE COMPUTERS

Then the next big computing step was the advent of microcomputers, starting with FRED (actually a TTL mock-up) in the late 60s, which resulted in the RCA1801/2.

Nice thing was all these micros added a whole new world of playthings.

New CPU LSI chips were produced: 4004, 8008, 1801/2/3/4/5, 8080, 8085, Z80, 6502, 6800, 6809, HP's Capricorn.

Yes, a CPU in a chip. Note DEC had started this with the LSI-11.

Very quickly after this, complete computers arrived on the scene, with MITS Altair, IMSAI, TRS-80, Cromemco, and Apple II.

I had by this date been building my own DAQ interface products for nearly 20 years. The new Apple II and later the IBM XT and AT ISA bus made interfacing a DAQ board very easy. You could even buy standardised ISA or Apple II proto boards for building on, with the bus (gold-plated fingers) and through-hole solder pads. Just solder in your chips, etc.

To program the Apple II for instrumentation solutions, I used a multi-tasking CPM based Cambridge Forth, running on a Microsoft Z80 Soft Card plugged into the Apple II bus. Yes, I plugged another CPU board into the Apple II. A multi-tasking Forth in these baby computers was a revolution at this time. Bill Gate's Apple SoftBasic was too slow for anything useful.

Also, IBM PCs became very popular DAQ machines after 1981, with loads of plug-in boards flooding the market. For PC instrumentation solutions I used Forth, Basic and Fortran.

Not many were using the Apple Macs for instrumentation from 1984 to 1987. The Mac didn't really have an interface bus suitable for instrumentation, only SCSI and RS-422. This all changed in 1987 when the new Mac II was released with a Nu-Bus plug-in board sockets, but still no DMA. You could also get a GPIB card for the Mac SE/SE30. NI had a SCSI – GPIB for early Macs.

An early RCA 1802 development board (1976)

I started playing with RCA, Rockwell and Hughes 1802 CMOS computers in the late 70s. These amazing chips were developed during 1969 to 1975. They were the perfect machine to run stack languages on, like Forth, as you could make any of the sixteen 16-bit registers the program counter. You can still buy this chip new, and they are still used today in space systems.

I used this amazing technology to build very low temperature solar loggers, for use on top of mountains in BC Canada where we were testing early solar panels in cold temperatures for powering remote communication systems. It would run down to –55 degrees C. These 1802's were all ceramic chips sets, and later some were SOS (sapphire on silicon).

In 1979, a colleague and I were invited by NASA to join the US Shuttle program. We had developed a very low power implantable radiation resistant biometric telemetry system for monitoring animals on the way to market (pigs in Manitoba). NASA liked the system and wanted it for the first space walk from the shuttle. However, we discovered it would take about two years to fill in all the compliance forms that arrived from NASA by UPS courier.

Instead, we burnt all the forms (five big cartoons full) over that winter in the living room fireplace and drank home brew every friday afternoon to celebrate the week.

(The first shuttle spacewalk took place on 7 April 1983 on the STS-6 mission.)

By the time 1986 came around and the release of LabVIEW beta 0.9 notes, I could build DAQ instrumentation and GPIB Test Instrument systems rapidly on HP-1000, PDP 8E and PDP-11, LSI 11, HP-85, Apple II and the newer IBM PCs.

However, the user interface with all these solutions was not a "Graphical Front Panel" and that is where the future pointed after the release of the Mac in 1984.

I could plot graphs but there were no FP analog and digital controls as such. Just text questions or function key shortcuts.

In August 1986 *Byte* magazine released the brief preview article on LabVIEW as technology of the future.

I immediately ordered a Demo LV copy from NI and waited. It arrived just under a year later in mid 1987.

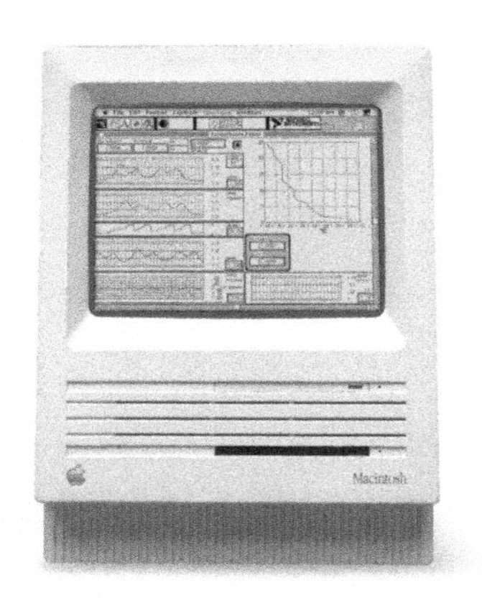

LabVIEW on a MAC SE (1986)

This is what *Byte* mag said about LV.

Introduction 82

Product preview. LabVIEW: Laboratory Virtual Instrument Engineering Workbench

by G. Michael Wose and Gregg Williams 84

Scientists and engineers can use the Macintosh as a general-purpose laboratory tool by creating Virtual instruments...

I then purchased the new Mac II with a 21-inch display and the rest is history, as they say. I am still using LabVIEW, and I still really love the method and freedom it gives to express my ideas.

At that date, July 1987, just to try out LabVIEW and to learn it, I decided to build a real-time metabolic analyser with the Mac II using NI's new NB-GPIB and a 32-channel HP 3497 as my DAQ unit. The NI Nu-Bus DAQ boards were not available yet. It was great fun. I also had an audience each day that watched and we all learned and played LabVIEW together. It took 10 days to build one of the most powerful real-time metabolic analysers of the time.

MAC II used in my first LabVIEW project (1987)

I still have that LV 1 program. It embodies much of this book's methods even back then.

From previous experience, it would have taken three or four months using standard Fortran or HP Basic to program a lesser version of the same thing.

And during those 10 days, I was also learning LabVIEW.

Previous to this LV work, starting in 1979, I used HP 85s with the HP-3497A DMM and mux switches to develop a series of metabolic measurement systems.

The following pic shows an HP 85, a specialist computer to drive GPIB Instruments. It had HP Basic, a built-in printer, screen and a digital tape drive.

The Mac II with LabVIEW, basically retired this computer after a stellar life.

HP 85 Personal Computer for IEE-488 (1979)

In September 1987 I moved to the UK to start opening NI's European offices.

They liked my LabVIEW work and my research background.

I was then teaching LabVIEW and LabWindows all over the UK, Europe and Scandinavia.

I also visited many major technology sites. More on that later.

CHAPTER 7
THE FIVE QUESTIONS

Focus: How to do LCOD Hidden Data.

THE FIVE QUESTIONS

The questions that I posed to myself to start the evolution process were:

1. How can we remove all and any types of LabVIEW constants out of the diagram?
2. How can we remove those constants out of the program to file in a disk storage?
3. How can we recover those constants from the file storage system back into the diagram?
4. How can we reinstall the constants into the diagram at load or run time or any time?
5. How can we make an online and offline editor to edit all those removed constants?

Let's look at Question 1 to start the process.

How can we remove all and any types of LabVIEW constants out of the diagram?

Step 1

Open the diagram.

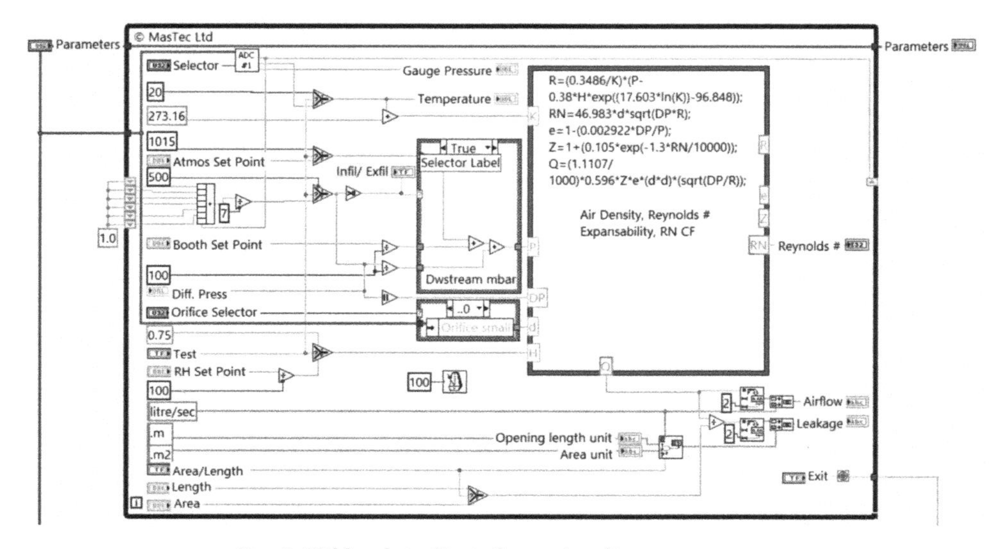

Step 1. Hidden data: Start of removing diagram constants

The diagram pic is an old program/diagram from years back called “Airflow Measure Orifice” that will be used to demonstrate the method to “Remove constants”.

I just opened some old work and picked this one to use as a demo of how old programs can be revamped easily.

As you can see, it has all the constants still embedded in the diagram. This is from many years ago, untouched.

Note: You do not need to change your old programming method of dropping constants around your diagrams to use this hidden data method.

In fact, carry on building programs as of old, being lazy, dropping constants in the diagram, and when you have finished building that VI, just follow these steps.

Step 2

Drop a constants cluster structure onto the diagram, outside the program structures, in clear space.

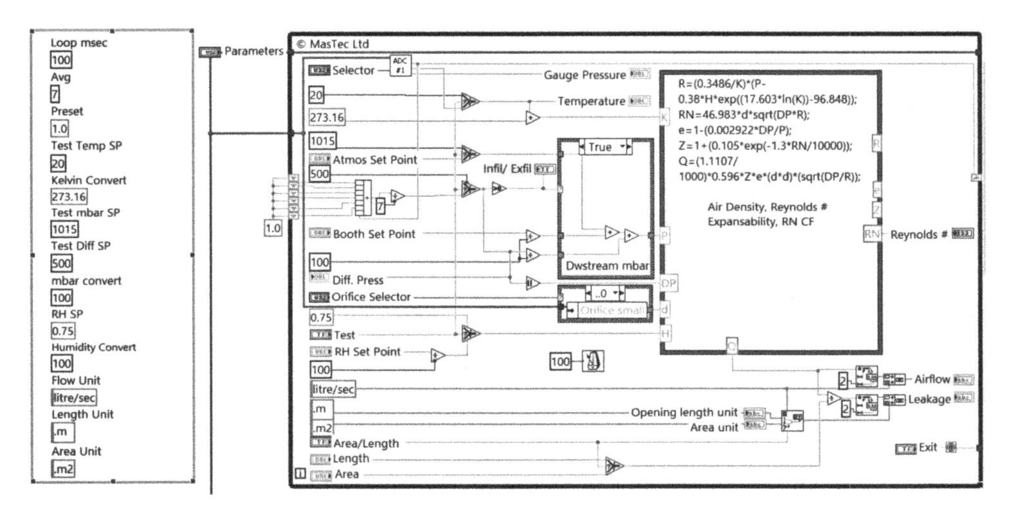

Step 2. Hidden data: Putting the constants into a COC

I use the left-hand side of the diagram and "Ctrl drag" all the constants from the diagram one by one into the cluster. This will leave the original constants in place in the diagram which will help later.

Next, rename the constants in the new COC meaningfully if they aren't already. Naming is an important skill. Not just for LabVIEW work. It is part of the creative process, naming things meaningfully.

Naming will be expanded later in the discussion. It can become very useful in auto documenting.

Step 3

Type Ctrl T, to tile the front panel and the diagrams.

Now drag that COC on to the front panel, for the automatic translation into a Control COC.

This step also creates the COC terminal in the diagram. It also leaves the original Constant cluster or COC in the diagram.

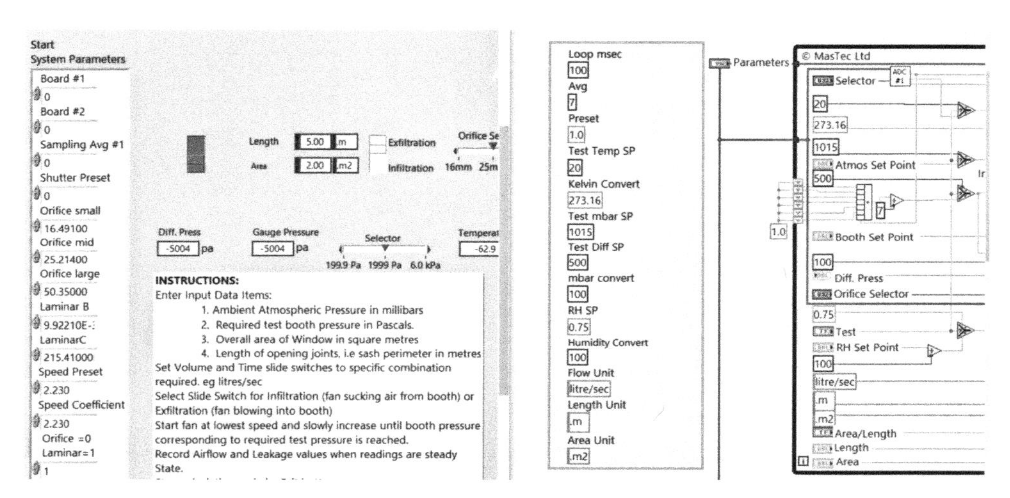

Step 3. Hidden data: Split the Screen

Step 4

Move the new control COC named "Constant cluster" to the left side of the front panel, out of the way of the original controls and indicators for the panel.

Find the new COC terminal in the diagram. Position this terminal in a convenient place in the diagram.

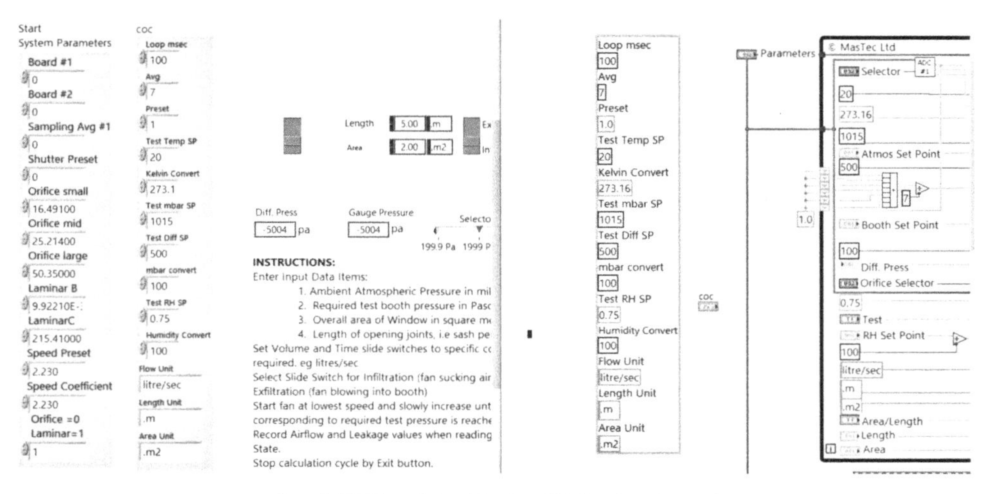

Step 4. Hidden data: Moving COC to front panel

Step 5

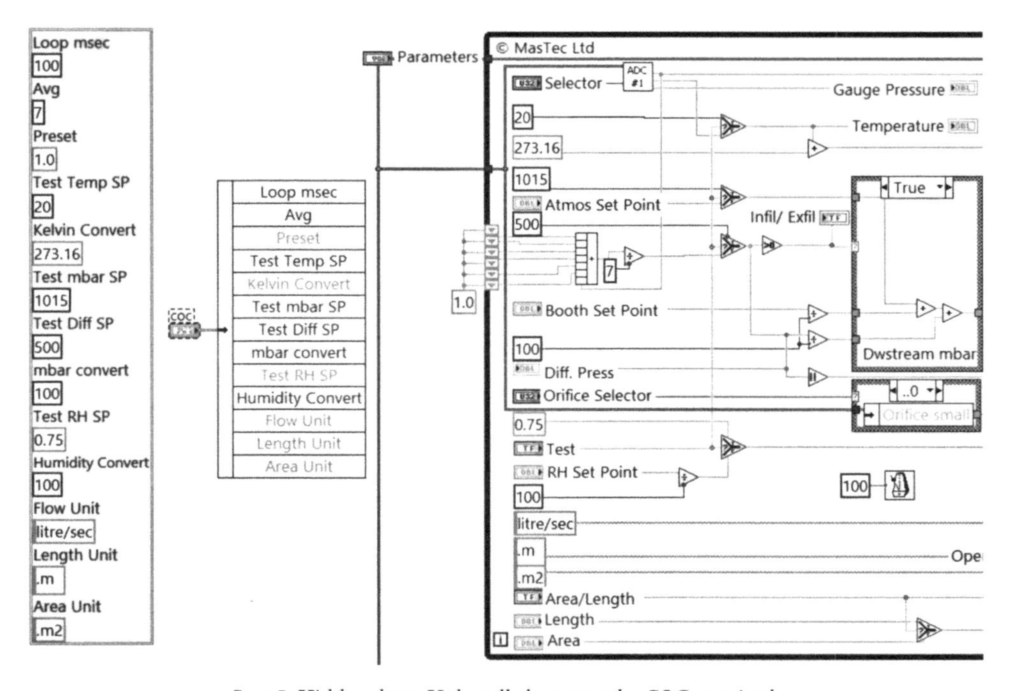

Step 5. Hidden data: Unbundle by name the COC terminal

Pop out the “Unbundled by Name” structure from the COC terminal and expand the terminals to show all the defined constants names, now almost sucked out of your diagram.

This is at present is just to have a look at them all.

Step 6

You can now delete the COC in the diagram; it is not needed.

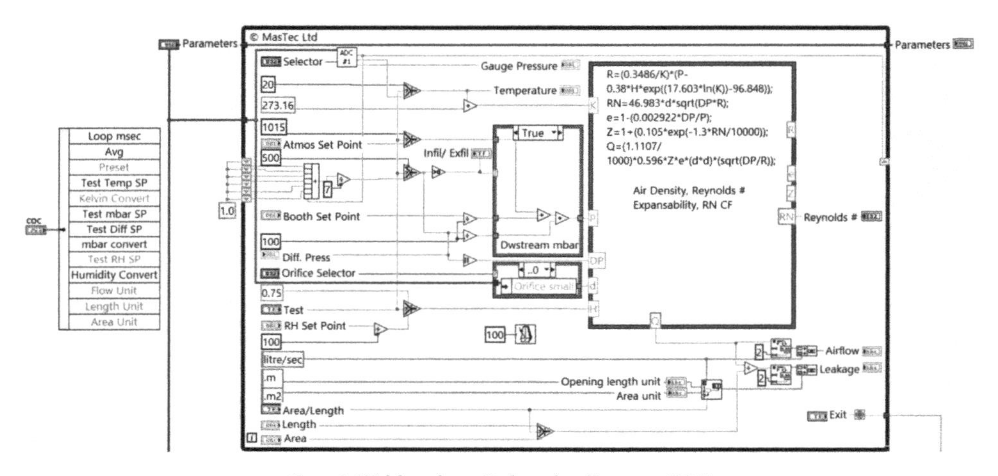

Step 6. Hidden data: Delete the diagram COC

Step 7

Embed the new “Unbundle by Name” structures in the main loop of the diagram like this or similar.

You may need to break up the unbundling into pieces to make everything look balanced and neat. You may also find that you will want to start dragging other things around in the diagram to make it neat and tidier and line up with the new “Unbundle by Name” terminals. Ecology.

Now drag wires from the “Unbundle by Name” terminals directly to the places in the diagram where the old constants are sitting. They are still in the diagram; you did not delete them. They are still wired into the diagram.

As you drag wires out of the “Unbundle by Name” terminals, wire up to those old constants, and you will start creating a bunch of broken wires as you do it. Do not fret at this point and try to fix it.

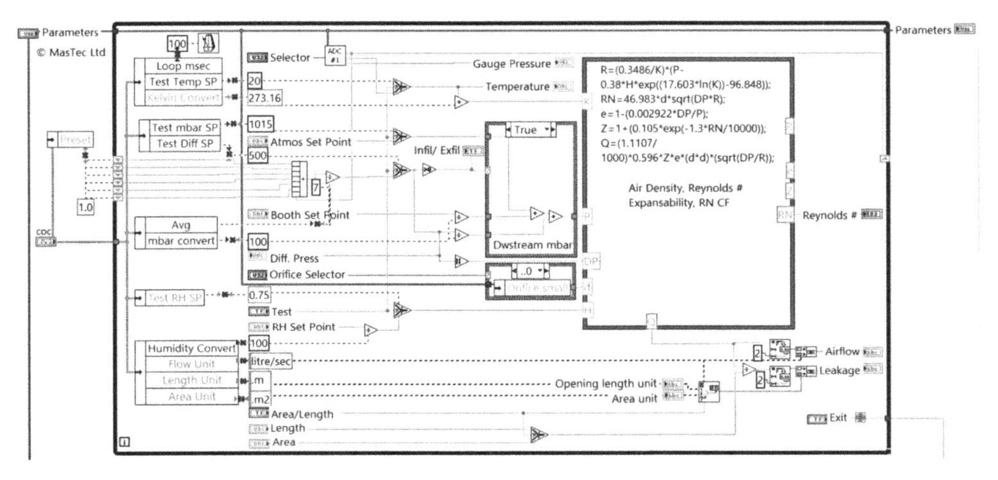

Step 7. Hidden data: Rebuild the diagram with the unbundled COC

Complete each unbundle terminal and then to fix the broken wires, just go through the diagram and delete the old constants one by one and the wires will clear of the error automatically.

This is when it becomes very obvious that the diagram is auto documenting off the Unbundle Terminals. The data for all those old constants is now coming from somewhere other than the diagram.

The diagram looks more structured and purposeful. To make it look balanced, use the terminals for the unbundle by name to all line up with the terminals requiring the constant data in the diagram.

All in all, this is a simple step and an improvement in layout.

Step 8

Just a last quick look over the achievement.

This is the final result of moving things around and balancing up the diagram again.

Does that look interesting? A new layout. No more constants. Just data coming back into the diagram. That was easy, and only one wire brings all those carefully named constants back into your diagram. Very simple.

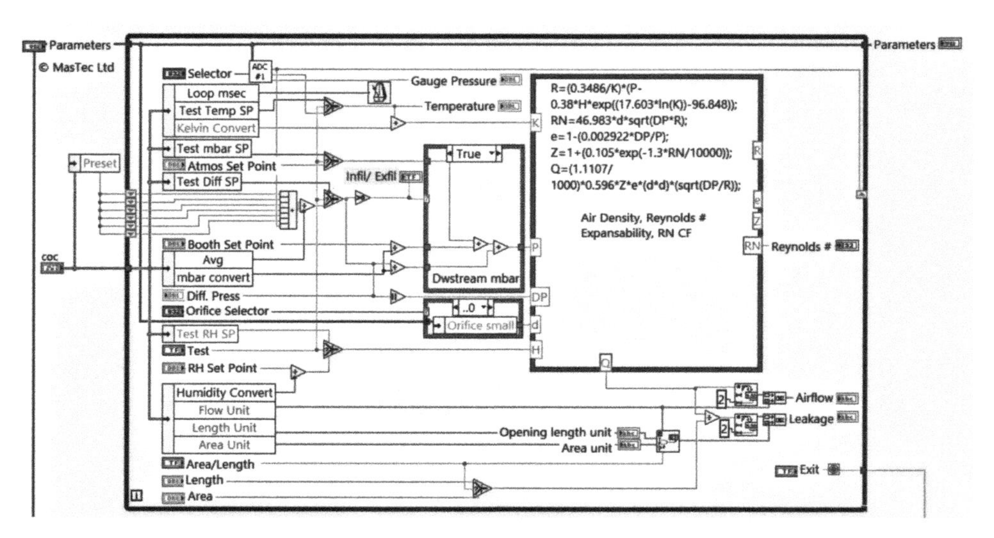

Step 8. Hidden data: Reorder the diagram to fit the COC data nicely

Last points about the diagram layout: I always put the name of the terminal to the right of the terminal for controls and to the left for Indicators to get more vertical white area. Notice the wires are almost all straight runs (if they can be), as this reduces "imaging high-frequency pollution".

Step 9

Now add a Tab Control to the front panel. Doing this step will allow the clean-up of the COC on the front panel and make each type of COC Tab section distinct. This program already had a public COC called "Parameters". This needs to be moved into its separate Tab in the Tab Control also.

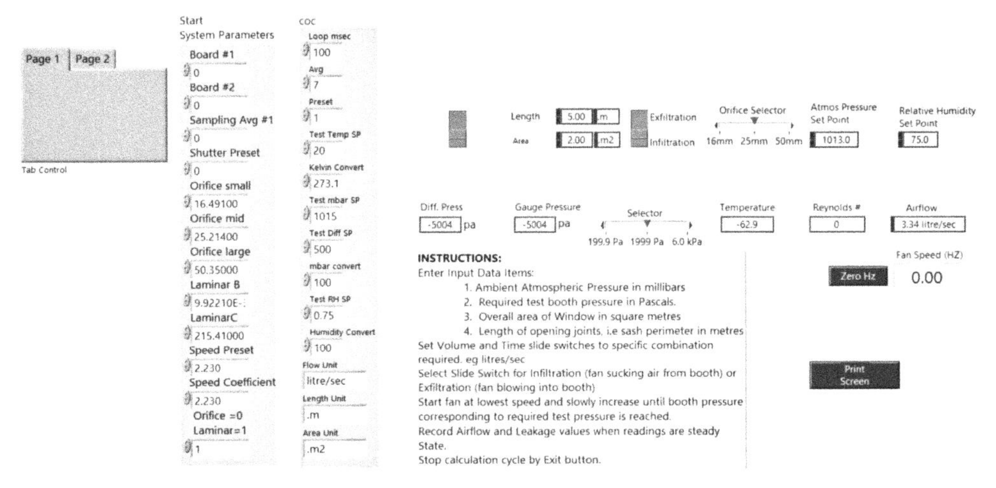

Step 9. Hidden data: Start building the front panel tabs

Step 10

Drag each of these COCs onto the Tab structures and name the Tabs for each COC.

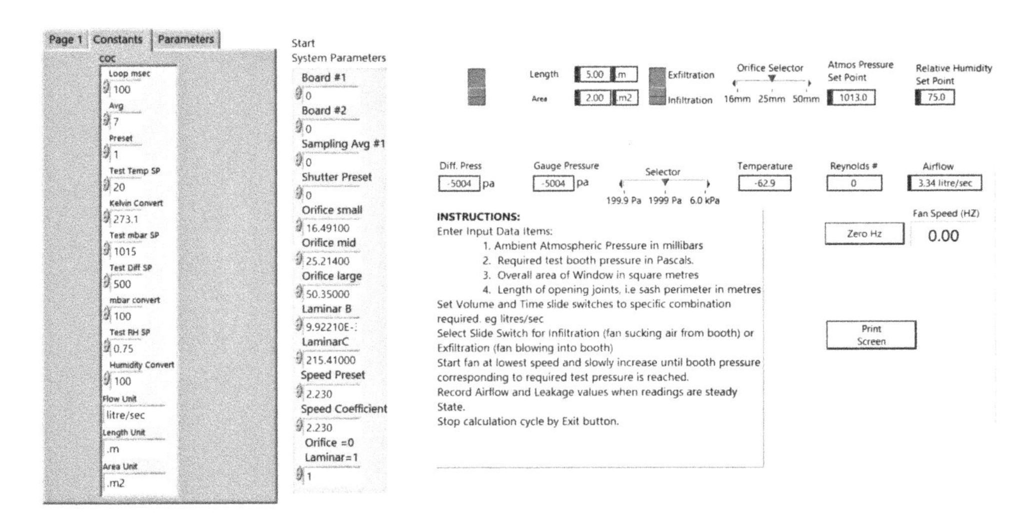

Step 10. Hidden data: Drag the COCs into the named tabs

Step 11

Select the original User Front Panel controls and indicators en masse and drag them onto a new Tab named Main Panel. Now that tidies everything up nicely.

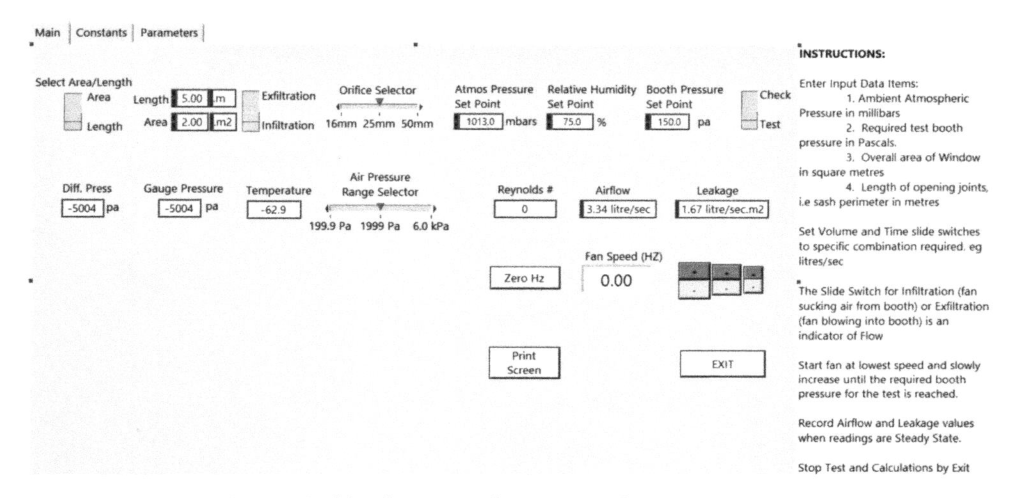

Step 11. Hidden data: Drag the main panel into the main tab

Step 12

Click on the Operate menu and select “Make current values defaults”.

Save the VI. All the control COC’s data (which were the constants) are now locked.

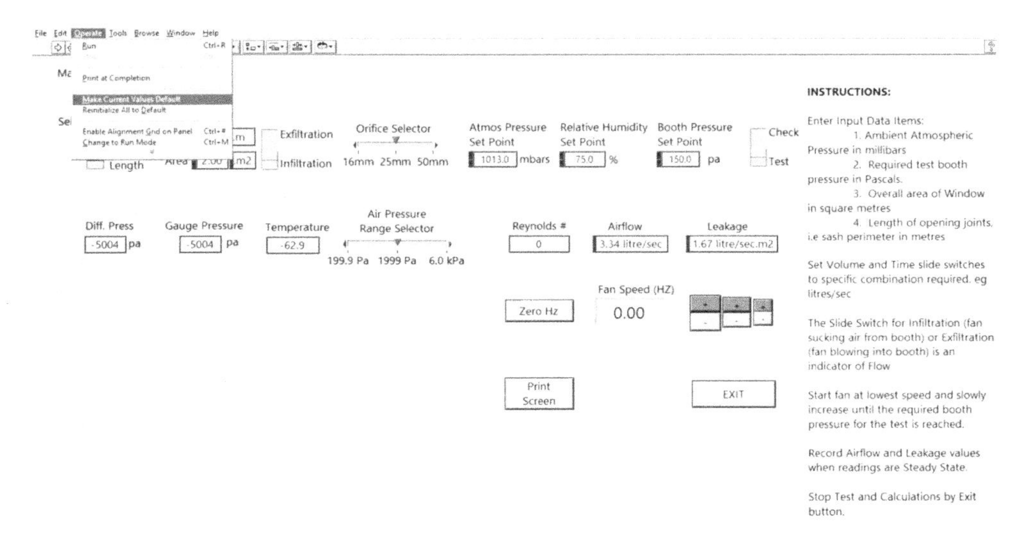

Step 12. Hidden data: Make all the data in the tabs the default values

We have now gone full circle. Each time you load this SubVI, the original constants taken out of the diagram are loaded back into the diagram from the Tab COCs where the values are defaulted to the original save.

This method adds one more advantage: it doesn’t muddy up the Main User Front Panel with trivia. All the COC, public and private, are hidden away in the extra Control Tabs.

Step 13

Last thing to do is to make each of the COC a Type Def. Name them well.

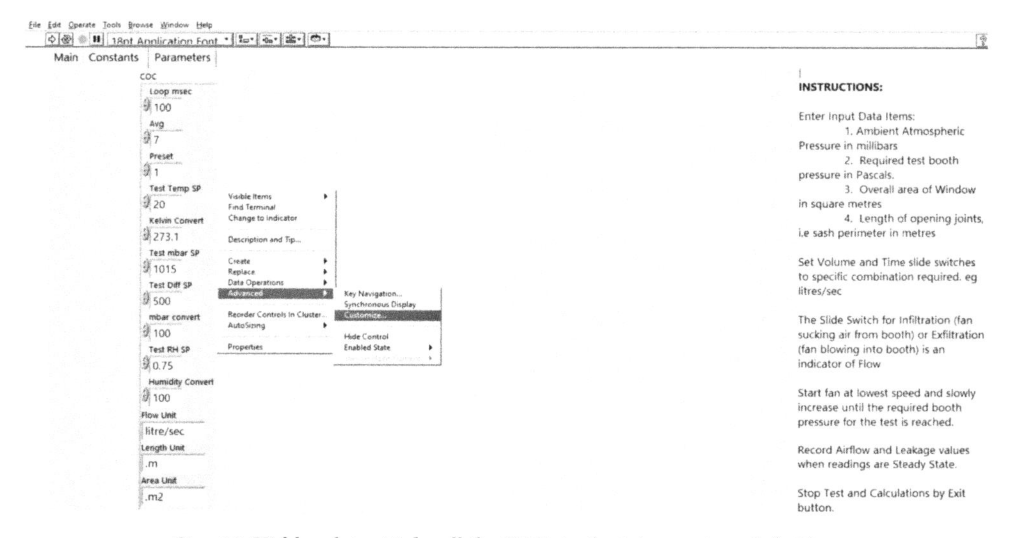

Step 13. Hidden data: Make all the COCs in the tabs as a type definition

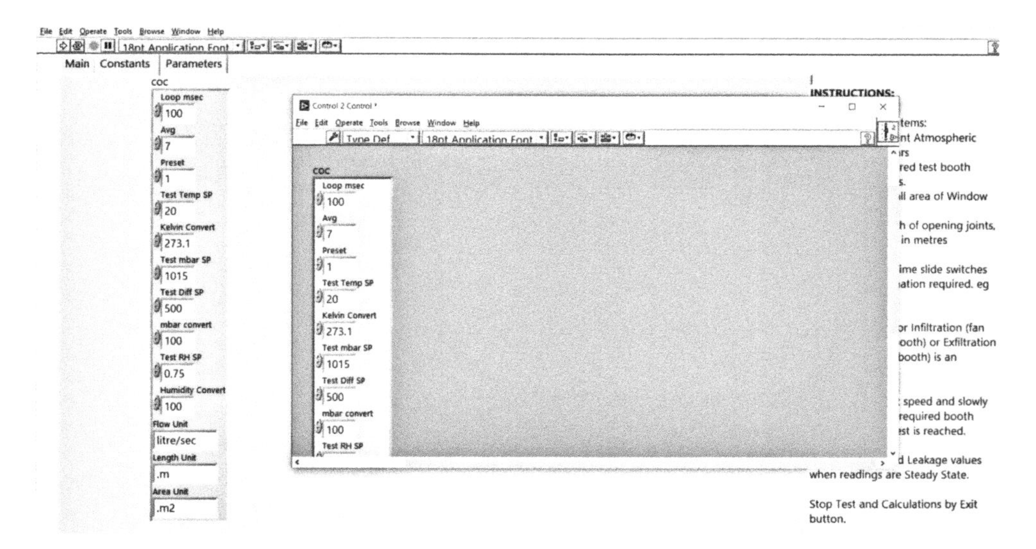

Step 13. Hidden data: Make type definitions

Question 1: *How can we remove all and any types of LabVIEW constants out of the diagram?*

Done.

A little postscript

Quick and easy? You now have a SubVI with *no constants*. That is the COC hidden data method about half finished.

Some will argue this is just giving the program more controls/variables. Yes, that is correct, and we could just develop with a control cluster as we work and drop new controls in the cluster when we need a new constant in the diagram. Well, yes. However, developing with a cluster in which you drop controls to make constants is a backwards and forwards sort of work, very slow.

The old way of developing programs, dropping constants in diagrams, as needed, I feel allows a more rapid intuitive build. Just power through the programming.

But you do whichever way feels best.

Then to make the COC, do all of the Question 1 steps.

The last part, of adding the Tabs for the COCs to sit in, finalises a rapid and all-encompassing conversion that tidies the diagram and the front panel well and with just a little time and work.

We still need to respond to Questions 2, 3, 4, 5 though.

We now need an easy way to save and reload constants from a disk file, and to stop using the LabVIEW "Making Current Values Defaults" menu method.

A little more recap

Do you feel that the diagram seems more abstracted, ordered, symmetrical, cleaner, documented and readable now? Unbundle by Name inherently helps with the appearance transformation.

We were very lucky to have these structures to use in our method. It is the basis of the method working. You can quickly discern the constants in the diagram as they are all in the un-bundles.

Also, you don't need to type a lot of info to make the diagram transform. Just name each of the constants in the COC carefully and meaningfully and the LabVIEW Bundle and Unbundle advantages of named terminals shine through.

You will also have seen in this example the front-panel Tab, the "parameter" COC. This is actually a "leftover" from the initial program development when the original method to make public COC was started years ago.

As we expand the hidden data method, this one all-encompassing "parameter" COC is replaced with several Tabs holding COCs that align with their function, such as ADC, DAC, DIO, Path, Master, calibration etc. The next few pics will demonstrate this.

You may have used something like this method before, so it is not really new. However, we are deliberately setting out to "Remove constants and to get them out of the diagram and then off program into file".

We are out of diagram at present but not yet out of program to file, although the process ideas have started.

So now your constants of any type and form can be in a COC, all mixed together. You can also align them and place them in the most meaningful layout, so at one glance you can see all the constants in that SubVI, something an ini file cannot do.

This new method is perfect for all Graphical Constants: switches, LEDs, enums, ring, paths, VISA, Active X, TCP/IP, and all those other constants/controls/indicators that are hybrids containing graphical properties that carry visual meaning with their text and numerical data.

For example, Graphical Constants to describe ADC and DAC channels, ranges and sampling rates, DIO ports and bit #s, comms ports, baud rates, TCP addresses, Modbus registers, Tables of data, cal data etc.

Creating a COC with Graphical Constants creates an automatic coding abstraction method.

For example, without Graphical Constants and trying to use ini files, some things become difficult or confusing. For example, if you were to use ini files to set an ADC input range of +/− 5 V and the setting number for the DAQ driver to set the channel gain is not known, then you have to get out the documentation and look it up. With an enum or Ring constant the selection +/− 5 V is shown in the graphical object, making the gain setting is instantly available and the abstraction to human concepts is completed. Additionally, all the possible settings are available and shown in the Graphical Constant. And of course, who cares what number defines +/- 5V range in the driver.

Often these Graphical Constants pop off the DAQ terminals already made for you.

Always build SubVIs icons that pop enum constant. (The front panel of the SubVI must have enum Controls for this to happen.)

This is probably one of LabVIEW's greatest strengths, the enum graphics control's text settings create the abstraction. No more remembering or looking up cryptic numerical settings.

As we progress, you will see that there is an even bigger win when the developer wants to change constants for any part of the program.

Don't make the names of the clusters and the names of the constants in the clusters cryptic, like normal ini names or use codes like MS Windows; use full names that are descriptive for you. Abstraction and documentation happen in the names.

We have achieved quite a change with this method.

Allowing the developer to see and modify all and any type of constants (inside a COC control) is a big step and improvement.

Next we proceed to Questions 2, 3, 4, 5.

But, a diversion first.

CHAPTER 8
TECHNOLOGY HISTORY 4

The very famous RCA 1802 prototype board, about 1976, my original one

Focus: A further look at the author's technology path.

UK AND EUROPE

I finished work at Simon Fraser University's Kinesiology Department in Sept 1987 and I moved to the UK, to start opening the NI European offices.

How did this happen?

After developing my LabVIEW Metabolic Analyser, I flew down to NI in Austin Texas to take the official first LabVIEW course. I found I knew most of it because of my project. So, instead, I just wandered around NI for three days meeting people. I sat with Jim Truchard, Jeff Kodosky, Bill Nowlan and a few others and showed off my LabVIEW work and talked technology.

They must have liked my LabVIEW project and my uni research background because when I got back to Canada, there was a fax waiting for me, offering a job to open NI offices in the UK and Europe.

I hired several people to help me open the UK office, also some help in France and finally, I opened Italy hiring Lino Fiore as the new director for Italy.

I was also selling product and doing seminars at the same time. I did hundreds of seminars and started doing courses on LabVIEW and LabWindows all over the UK, Europe and Scandinavia. I also visited major technology sites.

Some high points while in Europe:

I trained the Oxford Uni guy from CERN who built the first cyclotron crash cart; trained the European Space program group for satellite testing; trained GCHQ field engineers (spies), bus loads came to my training centre; connected LV to the famous Knock Octane Engine in the Department of Chemical Technology, Imperial College London; took the Base OTDR Noise Spectra readings on the first private fibre cable across the Atlantic; helped the British Navy test team develop LV Full Ship Test Systems (that is before the ship is built, test all the systems in a huge environmentally controlled warehouse); plus visited dozens of other amazing UK, Irish and European technical and medical sites.

British Telecom asked for help on the world's first "In Trench Fiber Welder". Airbus wanted a Position Monitor system faster than their PLCs that were carving giant wing beams out of large bars of aluminium with a CNC machine. That saved them loads of money when rogue PLCs and servos ran amok.

LabVIEW Developments

Here are some of my LabVIEW developments, structures and methods that came out of this time in Europe.

- GPIB Instrument Drivers. Built the first true set of Euro LabVIEW GPIB Instrument Drivers.
- The LV State Engine. This happened in 1988 at the first UK MacWorld show in London. An engineer at the UK Jaguar car company wanted a computer-controlled robotic spot welder. He needed a LabVIEW State Machine to do this. The LV State Engine was born at the show, using a while loop and a series of cases running off a shift register. Yes, in LV 1, the interpreted version.
- The Global Variable. Many programmers call this the LV 2 Global. However, they were available for LV 1 from 1988. Jeff K showed this to me and I used it to expand LV's abilities.
- Parallel Async Loops. Once Jeff showed me the LV 1 Global, the next step was to use them meaningfully and that was to make "parallel asynchronous loops". The first program to use this was my original LabVIEW Metabolic Analyser. I used it to make a separate async task to create variable speed or timed strip charts. It was the first async LV DAQ program, with data collected in one loop and displayed in another loop.
- Other Constructs like Flip Flops, One Shots, Counters, Stacks, FIFOs, LIFOs, Semaphores, Queues, De-Queues etc. were all developed in LV 1 while teaching LabVIEW at Cambridge in the Rutherford Labs in 1988 and later extended at Oxford. These functions were development, just to mimic some of the Cambridge Forth functions I had been using previously in the early 80s. It was all just for fun, to show you could make LV more extensible. NI LV development guys took copies to play with also and then built some of them into LV 2. This early work was all with the Mac LabVIEW 1, the interpreter version.

- One of my very smart students at Oxford started building the CMOS 4000 series logic set, just for fun, because he finished the three-day LabVIEW course in less than one day. He may remember and smile. So many 4000 functions, up down counters, flip flops, shift registers etc.
- MacWorld show in Paris in 1988 refined the state engine into a small demo program showing Async Strip charts in two tasks.

Some other bits

LabVIEW Silicon Solution

In early Nov 1987, I seeded Jeff K's mind with a letter about the Silicon LabVIEW engine solution, now FPGAs. He will remember and laugh. He said he did not understand. He was so pleased about that new revolutionary FPGA technology progress later and told me about it at one NI conference.

You may remember the early 1980s' Silicon Forth Engines from Harris Semi and others. Those Forth engines' microcodes were high-level Forth words and they had huge performance in small transistor count and very low power. One small Novix chip with 16,000 transistors could outperform a full SUN workstation in many aspects. It was able to do parallel execution of Forth code in one clock cycle. Now they have 144 parallel Forth engines on one chip running at Forth Tera-IPs, using almost no power. More on this later.

LabVIEW Programmable Properties: panels and diagrams using properties

LV 1 had static panels and diagrams with not many properties to alter just fonts and sizes etc. Also once you had wired up an icon you could not move it in the diagram. You quickly became very good at icon placement!

Again, in early November 1987, I sent another letter outlining all the extra dynamic features I felt LabVIEW needed. Many appeared in the LV 2.0

release, as a natural evolution from many users' requests besides my list. Now it is way beyond what I ever envisioned or use.

I built the first LabVIEW International LV and LW training courses and manuals (still have copies). In those early days, the hunger for LabVIEW and LabWindows training was huge. Just in the UK alone, hundreds enrolled. All the major unis wanted courses, so I drove around the UK, Ireland and Europe in a van for months with a load of Macs, PCs, Scopes, IEEE-488 and DAQ boards.

One of the more memorable presentations and courses was in the UK at Oxford University where Jim Truchard flew in from Austin to assist me in the course presentation. Yes, he drove around the UK in my big Ford van with me, doing seminars and courses. He may smile and say, "those were the good old days".

NI used to send over young application US-based engineers to accompany me almost every month.

The courses were a huge success, especially for LabWindows, as the UK in the first year of release, purchased 50% of all LWs sold.

Still have LabWindows 1 for DOS on a 386.

LabVIEW was a bigger ask, as most people in the UK and Europe did not have Macs but a lot did buy them just for LV, especially research and university groups.

When LabVIEW 2.5.1 came out in 1992/3 for IBM PC Windows, LV took off in the UK.

CHAPTER 9
QUESTIONS 2, 3 AND 4

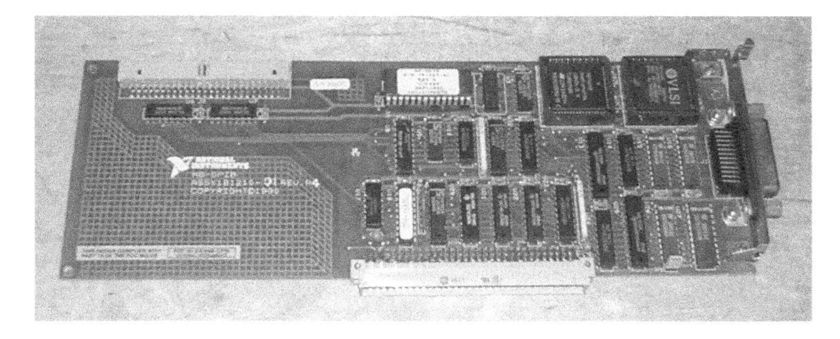

The original Mac II NB-GPIB Board that I used in 1987

Focus: answering questions 2, 3 and 4.

The original questions that were posed were:

1. How can we remove all and any types of LabVIEW constants out of the diagram?
2. How can we remove those constants out of the program to file in a disk storage?
3. How can we recover those constants from the file storage system back into the diagram?

4. How can we reinstall the constants into the diagram at load or run time or any time?
5. How can we make an online and offline editor to edit all those removed constants?

Now let's do Question 2.

QUESTION 2: HOW CAN WE REMOVE THOSE CONSTANTS OUT OF THE PROGRAM TO FILE DISK STORAGE?

You will recall that my original work of moving the cluster of parameter constants out of the program was to convert everything into ASCII and put it in a spreadsheet tab-delimited file. This was very text language orientated and it is limiting, because you cannot express Graphical Constants or controls through an ASCII file process like that and then recover them back to their graphical form. Much like ini files.

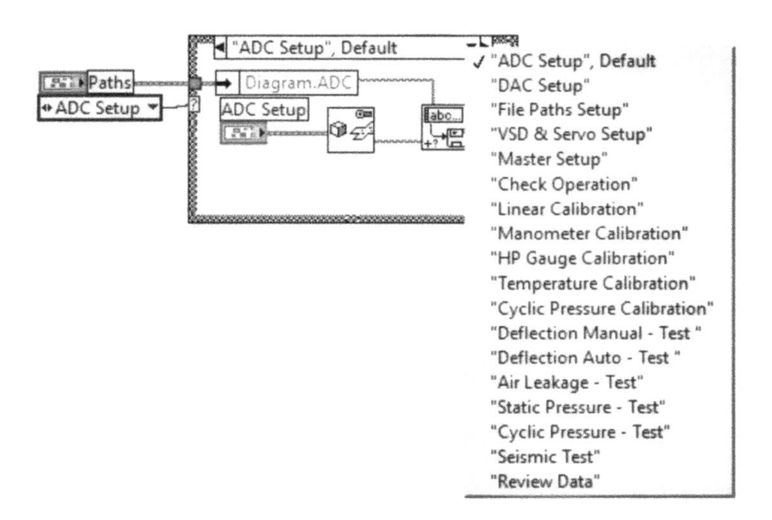

Moving the COCs to binary files

It is much simpler just to take the COC and Flatten to a String and save as a Binary File. This method will save the COC with any and all LV Graphical

Constants and also all the ordinary constants: numeric, string and other simpler forms. Done, simple.

This is how to save COC to disk. I cut this diagram snippet out of the original Editor program to show the method and also show the Editor's Save cases. Very simple: I like simple, and powerful.

Notice the Paths COC is used and is unbundled for each case step.

That is the end of Question 2.

QUESTION 3: HOW CAN WE RECOVER THOSE CONSTANTS FROM FILE STORAGE SYSTEM BACK INTO THE DIAGRAM?

It is just as simple as Question 2:

The pic below shows loading one of the public data COC namely DAC. Again, the Path COC is used to get the DAC COC File Path. A Local Variable "DAC" is popped from the DAC COC and wired to the "Type" terminal in the Unflatten from String function. This is used to recreate the COC from the saved flat binary string File. Standard stuff.

Note: the DAC COC local variable used in this example is popped from the program's in-built Editor where the original copies of all the public and private COCs reside.

Rule: Always use a Local Variable to get "Type". Why a local variable is popped has already been discussed but, to recap: this is done because as you build the COC as a Type Def, the contents in the COC may/will change, and the local variable just mirrors the changes through to the "Type" terminal and the COC is always the most recent and will be recreated correctly. Automatic updated shape or type.

We now have a very simple way to get the whole set of COCs from diagram to disk and back from disk into diagram and maintain content data and graphical shapes and styles.

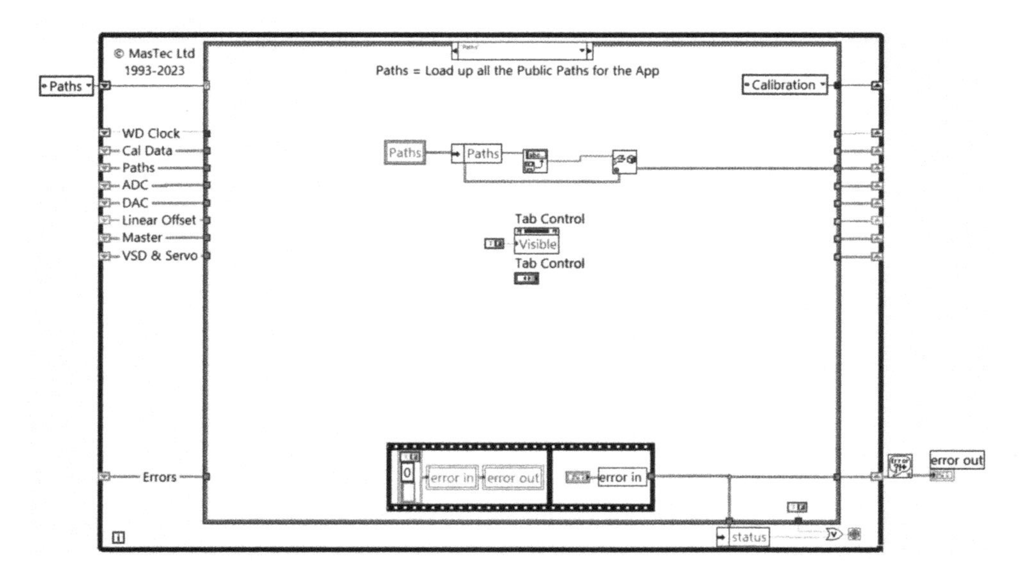

How to reload the COC binary files back to diagram COC wires

So that completes Question 3.

Pretty simple stuff but very powerful.

Quick and easy. moving COCs out of the diagrams into files and back to diagrams again from the files.

We've almost finished Question 4.

QUESTION 4: HOW CAN WE REINSTALL THE CONSTANTS INTO THE DIAGRAM AT LOAD OR RUN TIME OR ANY TIME?

Just a little more detail is needed to complete the whole conversion process.

Let's look at an example of a SubVI where the private data COC is recovery off disk.

Note: I will use the same SubVI used in the first set of steps called "Airflow Measure Orifice". It is a repeat of the last few pages but with more detail and it will complete the modification of the original old VI to the new "hidden data" or "Removing COC" format.

First the old Front Panel. I will convert the old SubVI FP into a new-style SubVI FP by adding in the necessary Tabs to sit the COCs in, then modify the diagram to do some initialisation and then load the COCs back off disk and move them back into the diagram.

Step 1

Add all the needed public Data Tabs for the Front Panel.

In this case, add the additional Tabs Master, Parameters and Paths. These COCs in the Tabs are all controls.

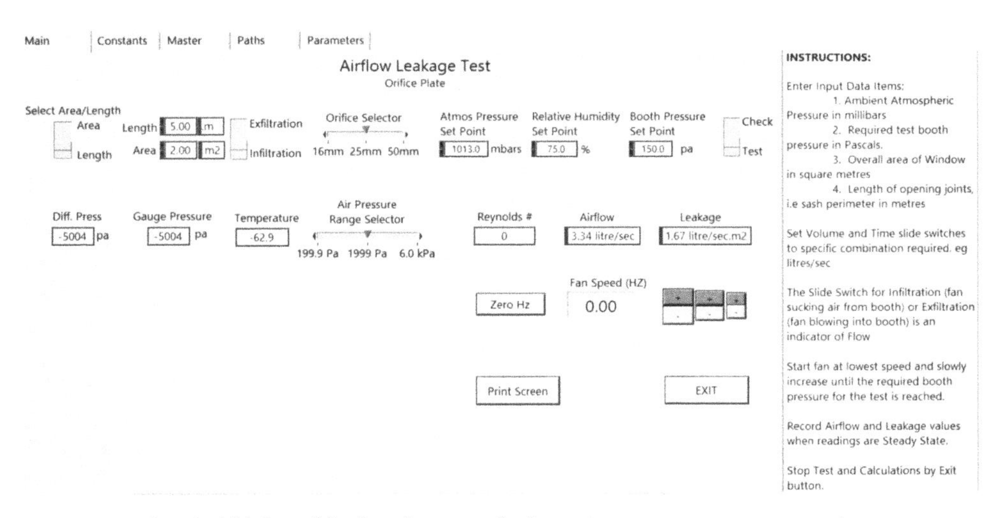

Step 1. Add the public data front panel tabs, main, master, parameters, paths

Step 2

The “Constants” Tab contains a COC that is an Indicator. It is private data inside this SubVI.

Notice: Inside this COC named Constants, I have added one more piece of info that is helpful. The meaningful names for the constants have now been expanded further and actually includes the value in the label. Look inside the COC and see those values in the name.

This is very helpful when it comes to working in the diagram, as you do not need to probe or flip to the front panel Tab to see the COC values; it is in the names of individual constants.

If this COC is a Type Defs (they must be by now), this new detail in the names will show up all through the program in the constants names.

Step 2. Add the private data front panel tab, constants

Step 3

The Master Tab has a COC that is a Control.

The Public "Set Flow Type" switch is a site-dependent thing.

Some sites use Laminar Flow Elements, while other sites use Orifice Plates.

The public "Allow Editing" switch is used globally to turn on and off All Tabs on all FPs.

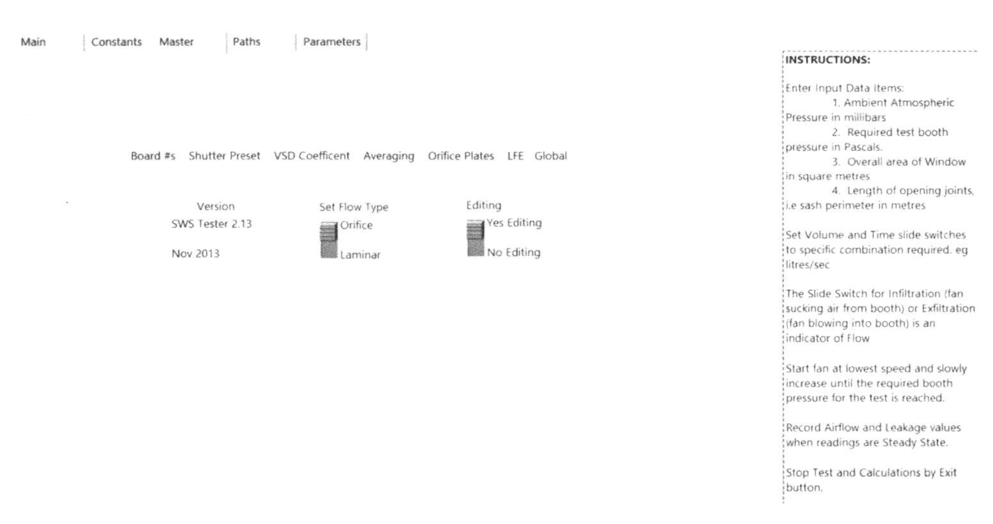

Step 3. Drag into the master tab the master COC as a public control

Step 4

The "Parameters" Tab has a COC that is an Indicator. I made this private data also.

Parameters COC is a leftover from early development work.

I have left the Parameters Tab in to show you can wrap up old work into this method if you need to.

Step 4. Drag into the parameter tab the parameter COC as a private indicator

Step 5

The Paths Tab has a COC that is a control. It is public data.

There are just two paths: Path for Internal private "constants" and public "Parameters".

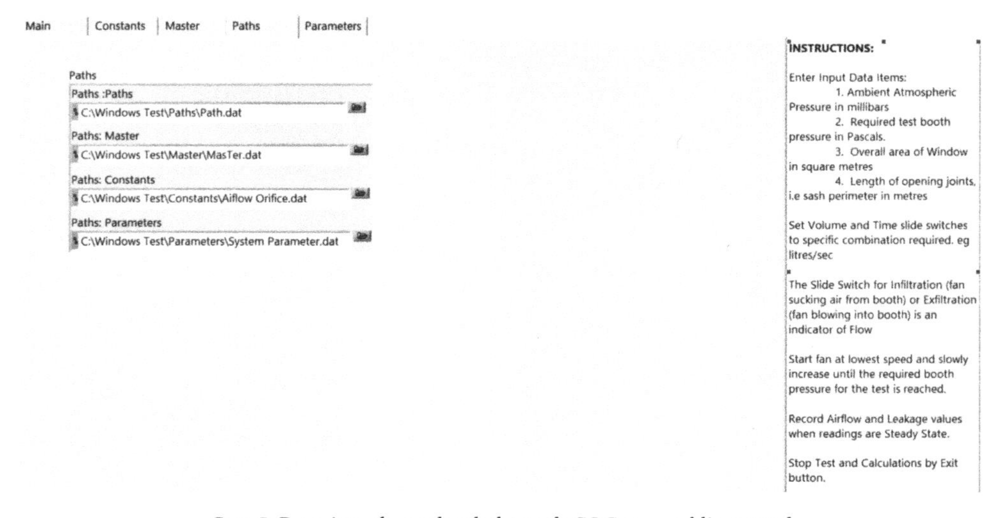

Step 5. Drag into the path tab the path COC as a public control

Step 6

Now let's look in the diagram. This is the new modified diagram for the original "Airflow Measure Orifice".

First, adding in an "Initialisation" state.

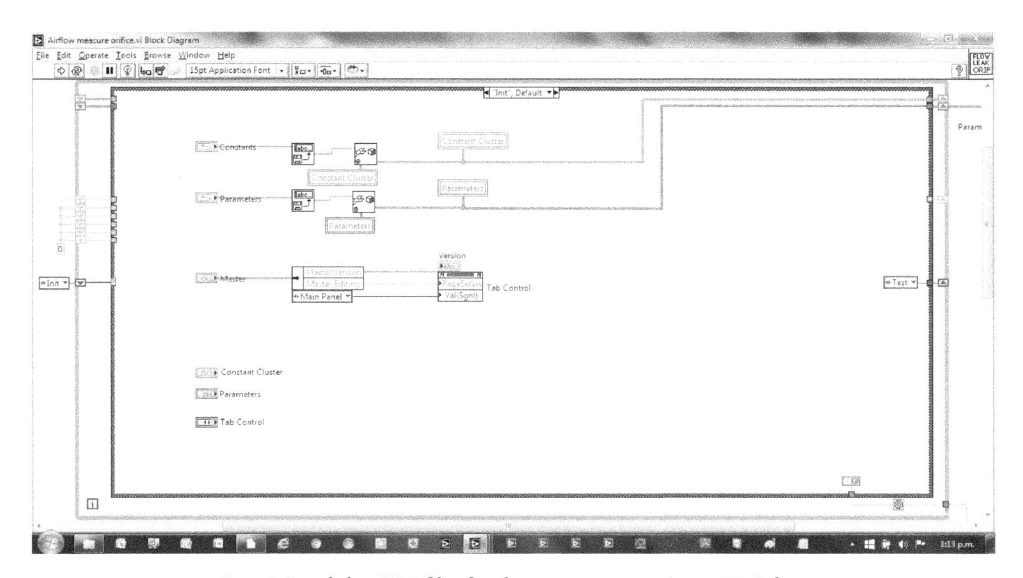

Step 6. Load the COC files for the components private COC data

This Initialise state diagram shows the rework of this old VI, with three states: Init, Test, Exit.

Notice that this "Init" case always runs and the COC are always loaded from the disk file.

There are three steps that take place in this "Init" diagram.

1. Loading Private COC "Parameters" back from the disk file.
2. Loading Private COC "Constants" back from the disk file.
3. Loading Public COC "Master Constants" back from the disk file.

The Unbundled "Master Version" supplies "Version" details to a string indicator on the Front Panel.

The Unbundled "Master Editing" Constant will turn on and off all Tabs globally. This is achieved by using the Tabs property node "Page Selector VI".

When developing, "Turn On" the Tabs, and when running "Turn Off" the Tabs. This Tab control switch is set in the Editor at development time or before run time.

See the next pic for an example of Tabs turned off by the Editor.

Also, the Unbundled Tab "Val" allows the selection of what Tab will show when the panel loads. It is always set to Main Panel, so the program always comes up with the Main Front Panel showing, not any of the other Tabs.

At the end the book I will add in some newer front panels to show where this idea is up to in 2022.

Step 7

Update the "Test" diagram. Putting the constants back into the state diagram "Test". We had done this previously.

Does that look okay, helpful?

Notice the new Unbundle Labels: now some have the values included. Very nice.

I always try to make my diagrams symmetrical and align the various pieces vertically and horizontally if possible. The reason is to reduce the diagrams' visual frequency, which is a distraction and makes it harder to concentrate and therefore read. Ecology.

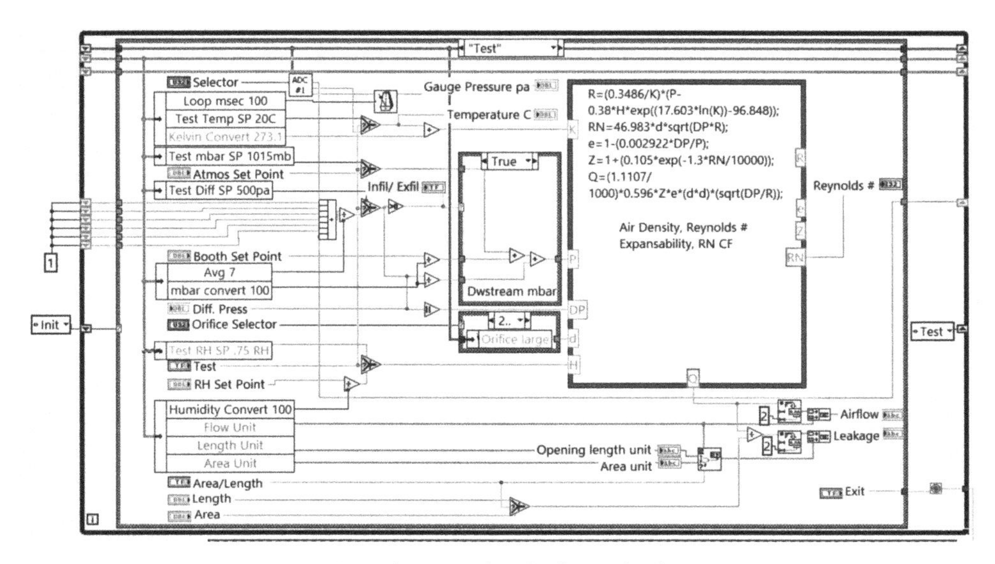

Step 7. Wire the COCs data back into the diagram

Step 8

Exit State: nothing to do with the COC.

We have now completed Questions 1, 2, 3 and 4.

We still need to answer Question 5 regarding the COC Editor.

I won't leave questions 1, 2, 3, 4 at this stage though, but will now show in the next chapter a more modern fully developed expanded program section to bed in the whole method.

CHAPTER 10

BEDDING IN THE HIDDEN DATA METHOD

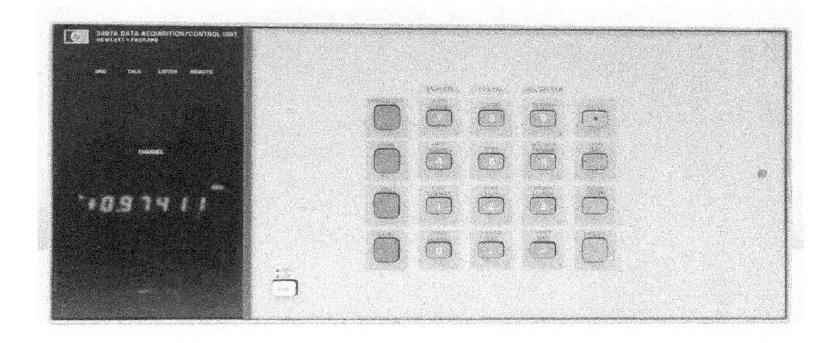

The original HP 3497A

Focus: Showing the program-building process again.

If you are like me, it sometimes helps to look at more pics actually to sink in what has been taught. I guess this is why we like LV, it is pictorial. Right brain driven they say.

Some more Technology before looking at this.

Around 1979 I got two of these. This GPIB instrument had a 6.5 Digit DVM, 32 Channel MUX (Mercury Wetted) for TCs, and 32 Channel MUX (Reed Relays) for voltage inputs. It was a superb piece of gear, and I used it for environmental, diving and metabolic systems. The sample rate (max about 250 Hz) and resolution (6.5, 5.5, 4.5 Digits) were programmable. I wrote the first rudimentary LV 1 Instrument Driver set for the 3497A in 1987.

SUBVI "MANOMETER CALIBRATION"

In this review, I will use a newer version of our old friend SubVI "Manometer calibration" to demonstrate the whole program-building process again.

This SubVI allows calibration of the DPM (UK) Auto Zeroing, Differential, Bi-Directional Manometer. These manometers are quite unique and have three ranges to calibrate: 0 to +/- 199 pa, 0 to +/–1999 pa and 0 to +/- 6000 pa that are perfect for this type of testing. Starting with the Front Panel, I will discuss all the Tabs used. I'll also designate them as public or Private Data Tabs for clarity.

First Tab: Main Panel

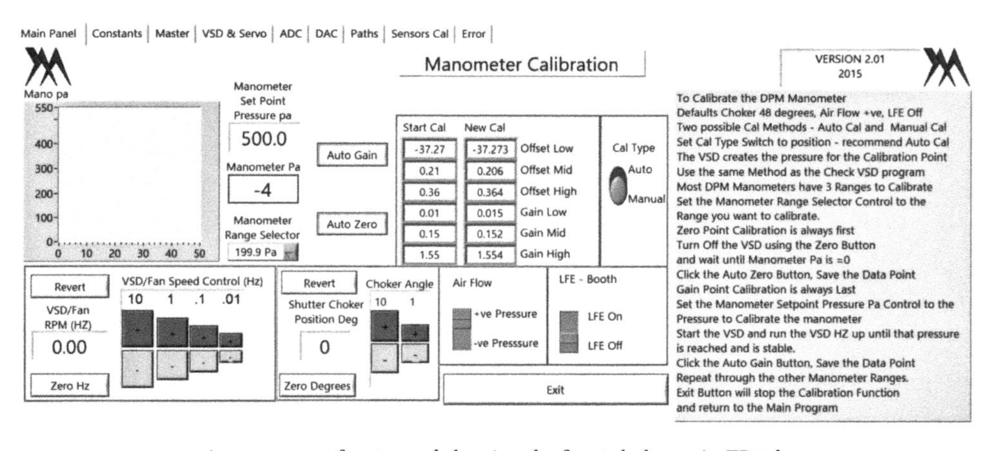

A more recent front panel showing the first tab the main FP tab

Second Tab: Constants (Private)

This Private COC data (below) is never seen in any other SubVI diagrams in the application. This privacy method creates a non-coupling solution. Inside the constants Tab, the COC named “Mano constants” is an Indicator. This private data is not connected to the public data terminals for the Manometer calibration SubVI’s icon. The COC data is loaded off disk. The Tab COC is handy to see what is loaded and just verify it is okay when developing and commissioning.

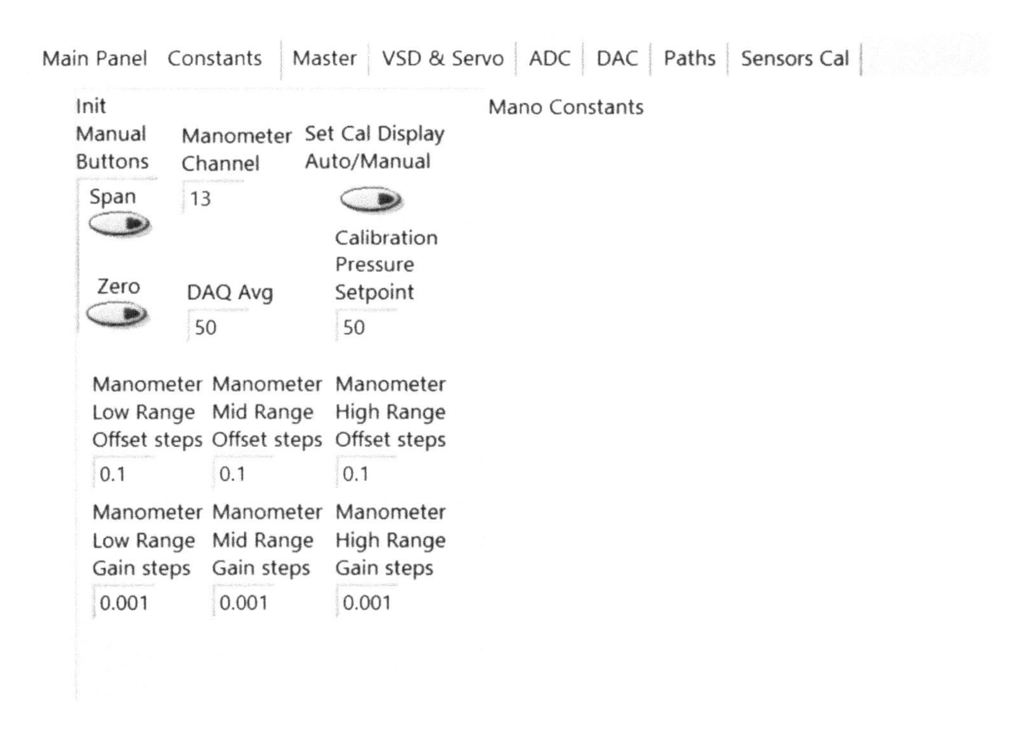

The second tab with the component’s private constants COC data

Third Tab: Master (Public)

This COC carries the version information and any system-level constants that are required.

In the Master COC, there is a switch that turns on or off the display of all the Tabs on the Front Panels for the entire program. This Test program has about 500 SubVIs. When Edit Switch is No, only the Main Front Panel Tab shows and all the other Tabs with private and public constants are hidden from view and inaccessible by the operator.

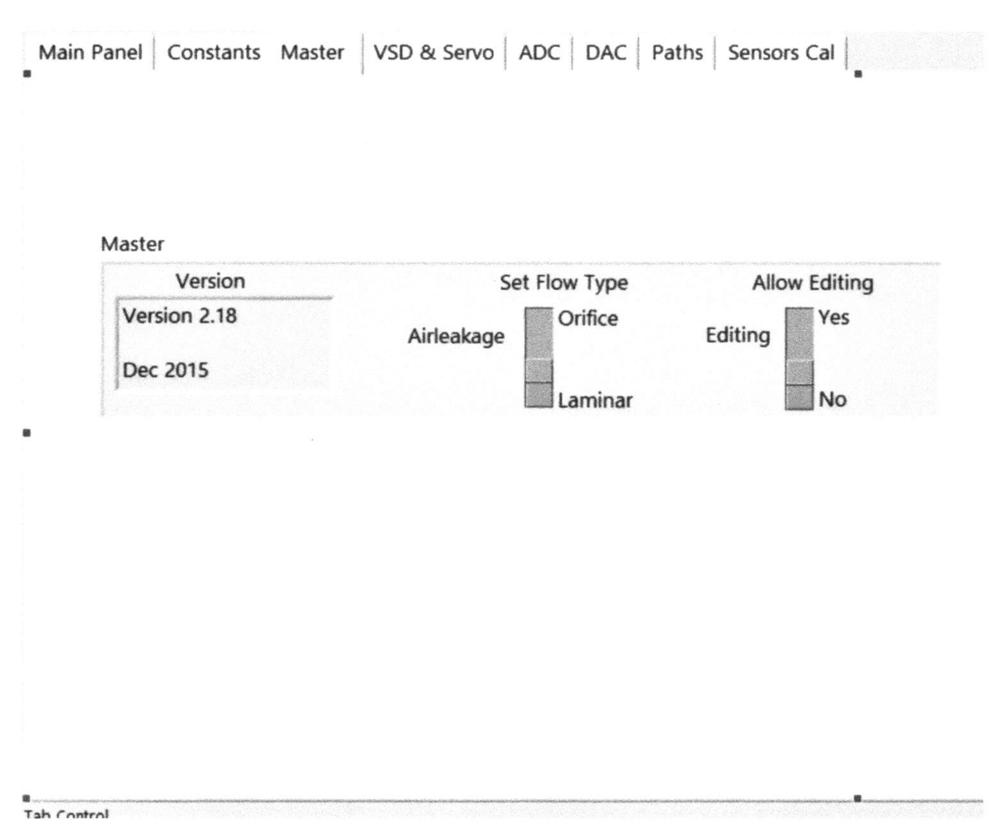

The third tab with the component's public master COC data

Fourth Tab: VSD & Servo (Public)

This Tab has configuration data for the VSD and a servo.

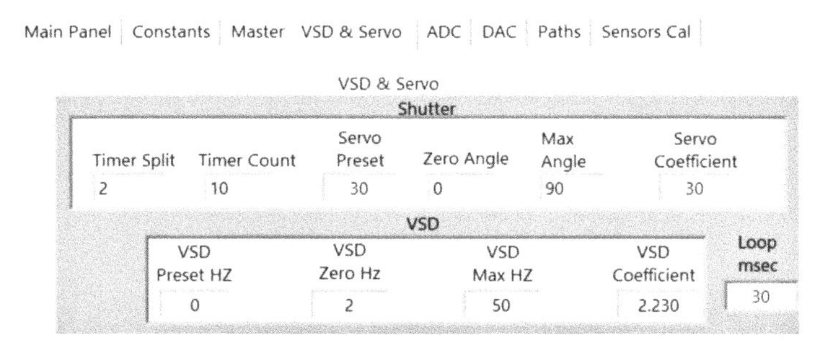

The fourth tab with the component's public VSD and servo COC data

Fifth Tab: ADC (Public)

This COC sets up the ADC for Single Channel and Scanning Channel DAQ.

These ADC Public COC are used in almost all areas of the program.

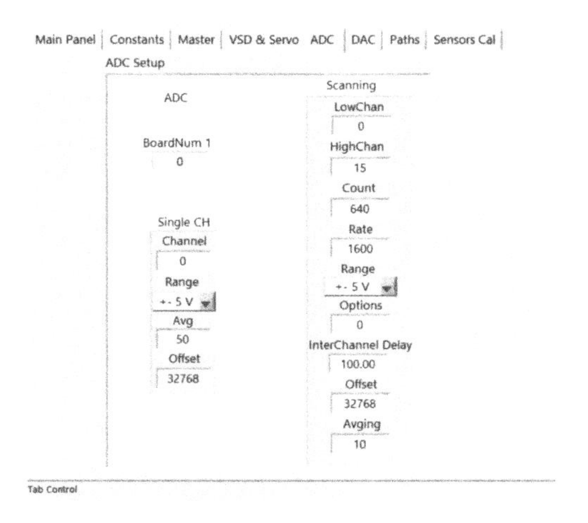

The fifth tab with the component's public ADC COC data

Sixth Tab: DAC (Public)

Main Panel | Constants | Master | VSD & Servo | ADC | DAC | Paths | Sensors Cal

DAC Setup

BoardNum 2

1

Servo	Servo Range	Servo Level	Servo Offset	Water Level 6	Level 6 Range	Level 6 Level	Level 6 Offset
Channel 9	0 - 10 V	0	0	Channel 6	0 - 10 V	0	0
VSD	VSD Range	VSD Level	VSD Offset	Water Level 5	Level 5 Range	Level 5 Level	Level 5 Offset
Channel 10	0 - 10 V	0	0	Channel 5	0 - 10 V	0	0
Linear PSU	Linear Range	Linear Level	Linear Offset	Water Level 4	Level 4 Range	Level 4 Level	Level 4 Offset
Channel 4	0 - 10 V	0	0	Channel 4	0 - 10 V	0	0
Spare PSU	Spare Range	Spare Level	Spare Offset	Water Level 3	Level 3 Range	Level 3 Level	Level 3 Offset
Channel 11	0 - 10 V	0	0	Channel 3	0 - 10 V	0	0
Cyclic PSU	Cyclic Range	Cyclic Level	Cyclic Offset	Water Level 2	Level 2 Range	Level 2 Level	Level 2 Offset
Channel 12	0 - 10 V	10	0	Channel 2	0 - 10 V	0	0
Spare	Spare Range	Spare Level	Spare Offset	Water Level 1	Level 1 Range	Level 1 Level	Level 1 Offset
Channel 13	0 - 10 V	0	0	Channel 1	0 - 10 V	0	0
Spare	Spare Range	Spare Level	Spare Offset	Temperature	Temp Range	Temp Level	Temp Offset
Channel 14	0 - 10 V	0	0	Channel 7	0 - 10 V	5	0
Spare	Spare Range	Spare Level	Spare Offset	Hydraulic %	Hyd Range	Hyd Level	Hyd Offset
Channel 15	0 - 10 V	0	0	Channel 8	0 - 10 V	0	0

'ab Control

The sixth tab with the component's public DAC COC data

This COC is for the 16-channel DAC that is used in almost all areas of the program. It controls a VSD, Servo, Hydraulics, Water Pumps and several programmable precision low-noise DC power supplies used for powering various devices, sensors and gauges.

Seventh Tab: Paths (Public)

This COC of Paths is used in many SubVIs.

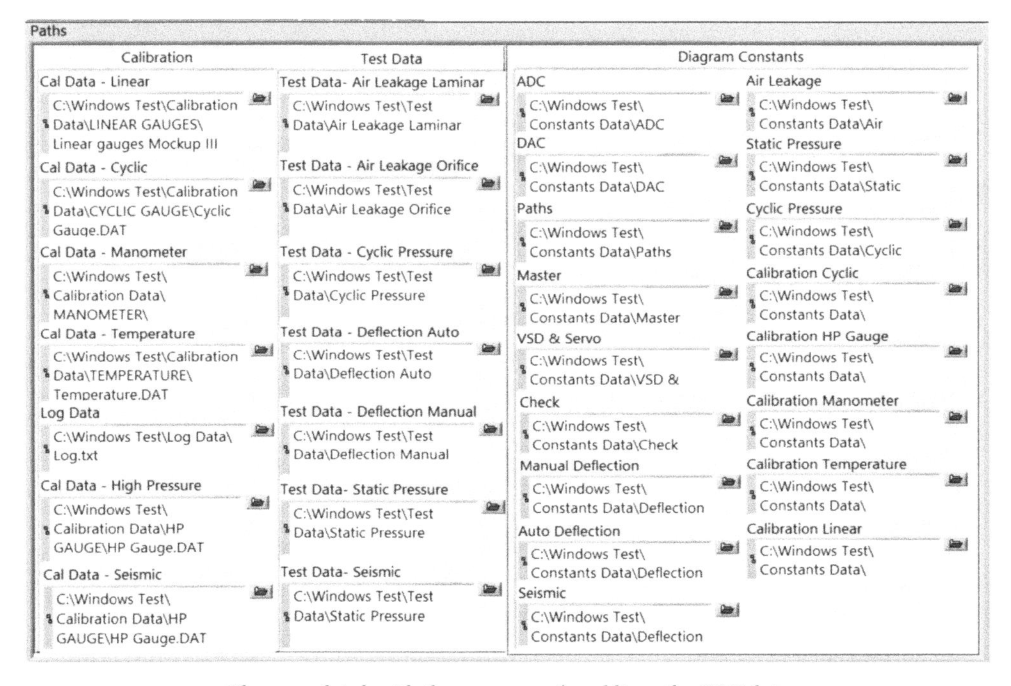

The seventh tab with the component's public paths COC data

Eighth Tab: Sensors Cal (Public Data)

This calibration Data is used in many SubVIs also.

There is also a Main Front Panel Operator button that allows expanding this data for viewing.

Calibration can only take place using the Cal SubVIs that are specific for each sensor or gauge.

At Run Time, the operator will only see the Main Front Panel with buttons and is not aware of the other COC Tabs, as they are hidden by the Master Tab on/off switch.

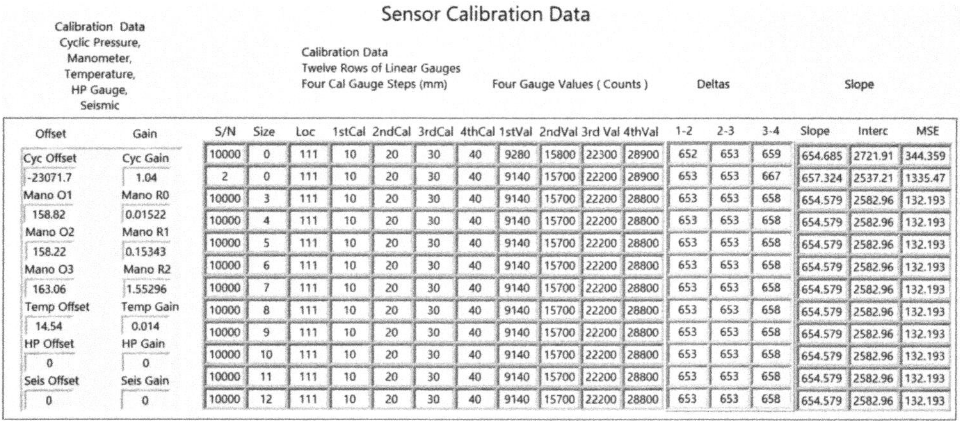

Sensor Calibration Data

Calibration Data
Cyclic Pressure,
Manometer,
Temperature,
HP Gauge,
Seismic

Offset	Gain
Cyc Offset	Cyc Gain
-23071.7	1.04
Mano O1	Mano R0
158.82	0.01522
Mano O2	Mano R1
158.22	0.15343
Mano O3	Mano R2
163.06	1.55296
Temp Offset	Temp Gain
14.54	0.014
HP Offset	HP Gain
0	0
Seis Offset	Seis Gain
0	0

Calibration Data
Twelve Rows of Linear Gauges
Four Cal Gauge Steps (mm)

			Four Cal Gauge Steps (mm)				Four Gauge Values (Counts)				Deltas			Slope		
S/N	Size	Loc	1stCal	2ndCal	3rdCal	4thCal	1stVal	2ndVal	3rd Val	4thVal	1-2	2-3	3-4	Slope	Interc	MSE
10000	0	111	10	20	30	40	9280	15800	22300	28900	652	653	659	654.685	2721.91	344.359
2	0	111	10	20	30	40	9140	15700	22200	28900	653	653	667	657.324	2537.21	1335.47
10000	3	111	10	20	30	40	9140	15700	22200	28800	653	653	658	654.579	2582.96	132.193
10000	4	111	10	20	30	40	9140	15700	22200	28800	653	653	658	654.579	2582.96	132.193
10000	5	111	10	20	30	40	9140	15700	22200	28800	653	653	658	654.579	2582.96	132.193
10000	6	111	10	20	30	40	9140	15700	22200	28800	653	653	658	654.579	2582.96	132.193
10000	7	111	10	20	30	40	9140	15700	22200	28800	653	653	658	654.579	2582.96	132.193
10000	8	111	10	20	30	40	9140	15700	22200	28800	653	653	658	654.579	2582.96	132.193
10000	9	111	10	20	30	40	9140	15700	22200	28800	653	653	658	654.579	2582.96	132.193
10000	10	111	10	20	30	40	9140	15700	22200	28800	653	653	658	654.579	2582.96	132.193
10000	11	111	10	20	30	40	9140	15700	22200	28800	653	653	658	654.579	2582.96	132.193
10000	12	111	10	20	30	40	9140	15700	22200	28800	653	653	658	654.579	2582.96	132.193

The eighth tab with the component's public calibration data

For the programmer, commissioner or support programmer, the Tabs can be made visible again by editing this Master Tab COC setting, with just one switch set to turn on all the Tabs in the complete application.

Development tip if you don't know this yet most will:

When you are developing and testing the complete application and a SubVI shows incorrect operation, use this simple tip. To allow you to troubleshoot the faulty SubVI, open that SubVI's front panel before you run the main program. When the faulty SubVI runs, it loads all the public COC data etc it requires. As long as that SubVI FP is not closed, the public COC data remains intact in the SubVI's Front panel Tabs with all the COCs.

This means you can run that SubVI over and over and get it running correctly without having to run the main program again to load the COCs. This allows you to incrementally work on that SubVI: edit the public and private data COC values and rework the diagram and when you have it all sorted, update the public and private COC data with the Editor. (Yes, we are going to get to that Editor soon.)

Always good to know how to make development easier. LabVIEW certainly is flexible when developing and debugging. It's an interactive component to play with. To do this in many other languages requires a little more work.

CHAPTER 11

BUILDING THE MAIN PROGRAM FRONT PANEL

The Mac II Nubus IEEE-488 and DAQ boards expanded LabVIEW's ability greatly. Thank you, Apple and NI.

Focus: building a new program which will lead to the following chapter on the COC Editor.

The Mac IIx design above had a Motorola 68030 CPU at 16 MHz. I had one with 128 Megs of memory, which was astounding back then. My Mac had a 21-inch white display. I can't remember the manufacturer, but it wasn't Apple.

MAIN PROGRAM FRONT PANEL

The final steps in the hidden data method before we build the COC Editor into the Main Front Panel using one of the Tabs.

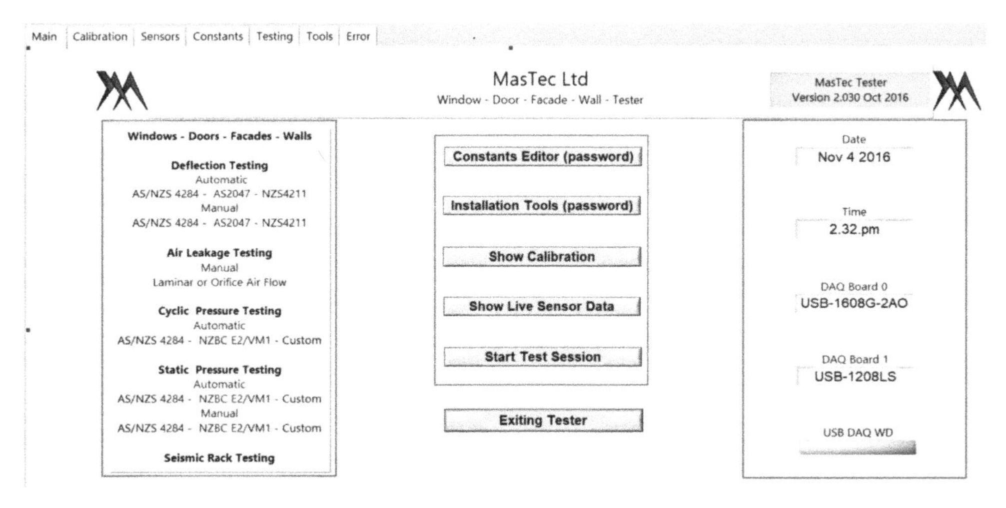

The main tab's FP has a button to bring forward the COC editor tab

Tab Main

The Tab Main is the default and has the buttons that open the other Tab panels. The button "Show calibration" displays the Tab calibration as the new FP with data tables with some stats.

This button is added to the program to allow the operator to ascertain if the calibration data they are using is correct and current before they start testing.

These programs are for a certified tester and must use certified calibration data off certified sensors.

Button: Show Live Sensor Data

The button "Show Live Sensor Data" displays the Tab Sensors as the new FP and starts running the Test Rig DAQ in real time showing the data from the sensors. The Sensors displayed are Manometer, Temperature, Cyclic Pressure and Linear Gauges etc.

Notice the data is displayed in engineering units or EUs, abstracting ADC volts to mm, Pa, deg C. This is to allow the operator to ascertain if all the sensors are running and giving true data.

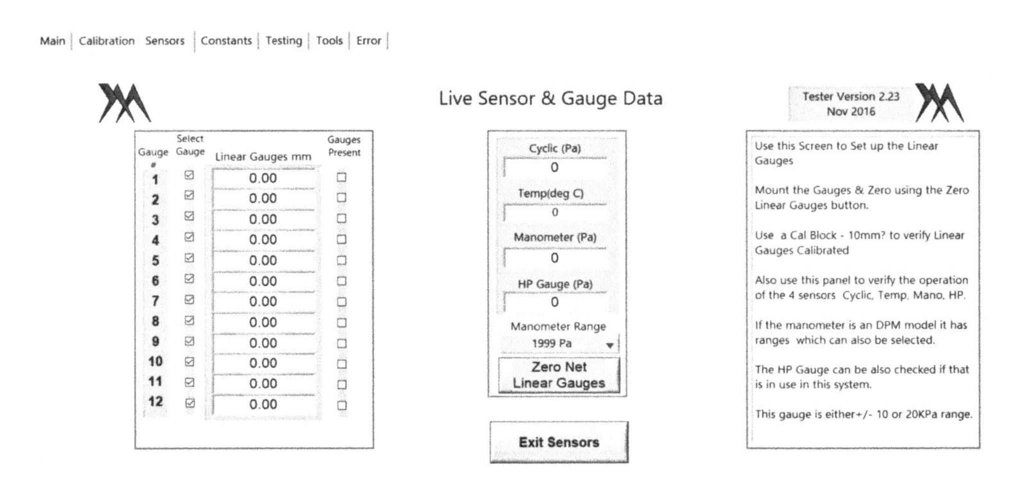

The main tab's FP has a button to bring forward the live sensor data tab

Usually, for the deflection data, the operator will take a walk out to the pressure tester chamber with mounted UUT and where the deflection gauges are mounted and slide into any of the deflection gauges a certified calibration Test Block of 10 or 25 mm. Back at the Test Computer, the mm data will be revealed. This is reassuring for the operator. If they didn't do the short walk, they may well be wasting their time testing, only to discover later that all is not well with the sensors and the data.

The deflection gauges used in these Testers are all calibrated to a specific ADC channel and have their own extension cables. The operators go to great effort to calibrate all of these gauges, up to 48 of them, using a four or five-point calibration routine.

The gauge deflection in Engineering Units (EU) is calculated using least squared linear fit or using a 4-point polynomial equation. The gauges and their specific cables are carefully stored away after each test, with the cables neatly rolled up.

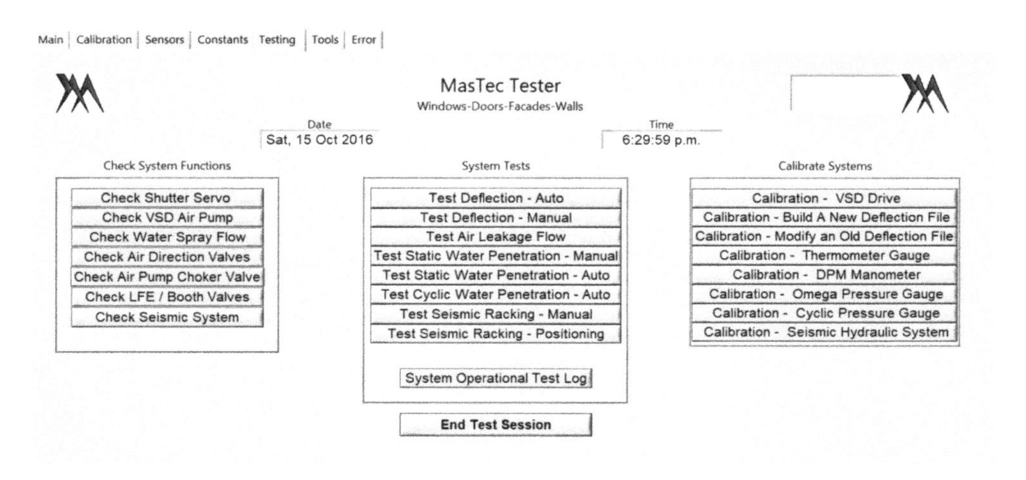

The main tab's FP has a button to bring forward the start test session tab

Button: Start Test Session

The button "Start Test Session" displays the Tab "Testing" as the new FP. This allows access to all the Tester's functionality.

This almost wraps up the Front Panel Design. There will be more complex versions later.

However, we have not looked at the remaining Tab "constants".

This is where the COC Editor resides on the main FP of the application.

Yes, at last Question 5 next chapter.

Test Systems

A little more on these Test Systems. (Just out of interest.)

The actual mechanical Pressure Vessel part of these Test Rigs ranges in size from simple single-storey height units to giants four storeys high. It is a huge steel pressure box, up to 10 metres wide by 10 metres high and about 4 to 5 metres deep.

These Test Rigs can have up to 48 Linear Displacement Gauges in a matrix across the front of the UUT (usually a building facade or giant windows).

They also can have a Hydraulic Pump and RAM, with a seismic control system that moves or shakes the UUT with lateral forces.

There are also calibrated water-sprayer nozzles in a matrix at up to six levels high with 30–42 nozzles inside the test booth. The water system is controlled by a PLC with six PIDs running on servo-controlled water valves. This is for water penetration testing.

For leakage testing, Laminar flow elements (LFE) or orifice plates with high-accuracy differential pressure gauges measure flow in and out of the Test Pressure Box, under standardised pressures.

Air pressure is made by a combo VSD driving a high-horsepower motor and fan (up to 65 hp).

The installation and build-up of a new UUT can take two to four weeks, depending on the complexity. A UUT can be as complex as a multi-storey building facade (walls, windows, doors, balcony, cladding etc.) for “a repeating section” of a multi-storey apartment block. These UUTs are built into the Test Pressure box by a team of carpenters and techs.

A test can sometimes take a week or two to complete.

A standardised certified signed-off report is issued on all tests.

This is all about compliance, insurance, building permits, guarantees and the like.

In other tests, it can be verification for a new design of aluminium extrusions used in windows and doors etc.

The design teams come down and watch their new babies being tested and it can become circular as failures lead to better designs and then better products by the fabricators.

Quite the deal.

CHAPTER 12
BUILDING THE COC EDITOR

Focus: Finally, Question 5: making an easy-to-use editor to work on all hidden data COCs.

The questions that I posed to myself to start the evolution process were:

Why this scanner? Notice the GPIB plug on the side. There is quite a story with this: more later.

1. How can we remove all and any types of LabVIEW constants out of the diagram?
2. How can we remove those constants out of the program to file in a disk storage?
3. How can we recover those constants from the file storage system back into the diagram?
4. How can we reinstall the constants into the diagram at load or run time or any time?
5. *How can we make an online and offline editor to edit all those removed constants?*

In the previous chapter, we did look closely at the Main Program Front Panel Tab “constants”.

This is where our COC Editor resides for managing all public and private COC data. Yes, the editor is included right in the Main Front Panel of the program. It is password protected.

In this chapter I will use a newer version Main Program Front Panel (next pic) to show the Editor that resides in the Tab "Constants".

BUILDING THE EDITOR INTO THIS NEW EXPANDED MAIN FRONT PANEL

This is a newer Front Panel with two more Tabs (Tools and Error). I am evolving and expanding the method to show there is great freedom in this design.

The COC Editor functionality required is loading, saving and editing of all the COC data.

This is the Editor's Front Panel Tabs where all COCs reside. It is quite extensive.

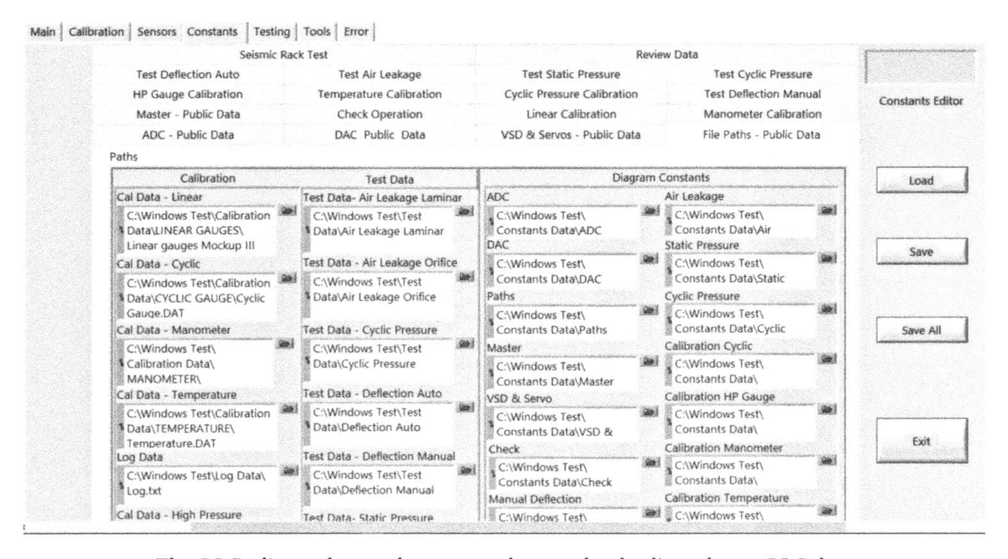

The COC editor, a large tab structure that can load, edit and save COC data

All the COCs reside also in another Tab Control with all those subTabs shown.

The subTab displayed is file “Paths” – public Data. It is actually a large cluster with two sub-clusters contained in the COC. The cluster on the right contains the paths to the SubVI diagram private data COC files. The cluster on the left has the paths to the calibration and Test data files. They are named as such.

Now into the bones of the Editor.

The diagram for the Editor is just a simple six-stage state engine. I have built more complex editors that go way beyond this simple one. This is all you need though.

Editor States

The Editor States: Init, Idle, Load, Save, Save All, and Exit; these are controlled with four buttons:

- Load Button – Loads all the data for the COC in all the Tabs from files using “Paths”
- Save Button – Saves the current selected subTab COC data to file using “Paths”
- Save All Button – Saves all the subTabs COC data to files using “Paths”
- Exit Button – Just that.

So let’s see how it is built into the main program and functions.

The next few pics are the “Editor” state engine diagrams.

The Initialisation State

The first addition to building the COC Editor into the main program is just adding another subTab to the main Front Panel Tab named “constants”.

Then insert into this “Constants” Tab control another set of multi subTab Controls that have all the subTabs sections for all the program’s COCs, as in the previous pict.

Yes, it is quite extensive now.

This “constants” Tab allows displaying and modifying all the data in the COC for the whole program. Just click on the COC Tab you want and adjust the COC values.

This is a very big step and powerful.

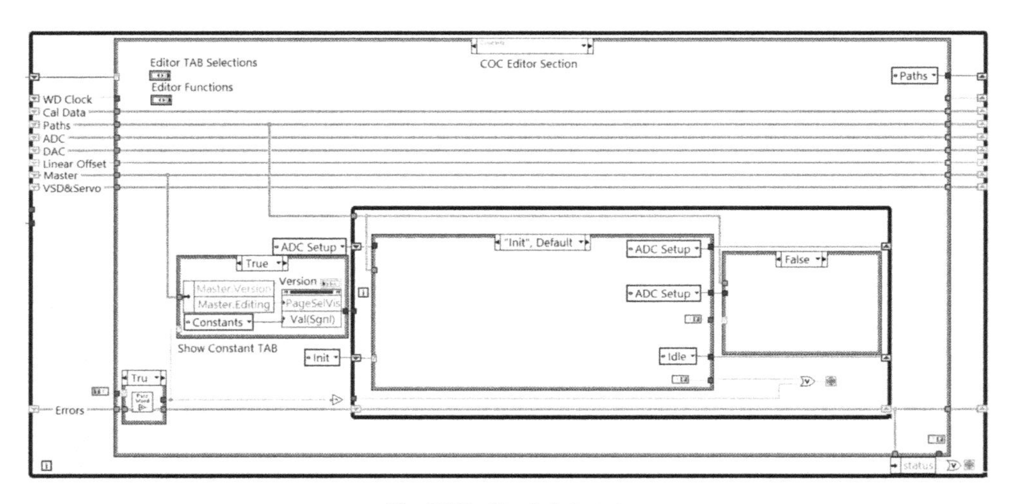

The COC editor’s Init state

The Editor State Engine diagram is quite simple.

It is just a simple state engine with two sets of parallel cases that allow loading and saving COC data from disk.

On Entry into the Editor State:

The first thing to note, this is not a SubVI. It is just one frame in the main diagram. The COC editor resides inside the main program state engine inside just one state.

It could be built as a SubVI that pops its front panel with all the COCs displayed if you like. I have made this type of program also. Make it either way.

In fact, if you build an external standalone VI Editor program, this can become the SubVI editor.

You choose.

To access the Editor, click the Front Panel button "Show Constants" and the Tab Panel "constants" now becomes the Main FP of the Application.

The first State to run is "Idle".

Note: there are two parallel cases in this state.

The right case in the state engine is set to False in "idle" or no activity at this point.

This "Idle" state brings up the Editor into a safe and "wait for buttons" state.

Idle State

The Editor now just runs the Idle State looping and it waits for any of the Editor buttons to be clicked: Load, Save, Save All, Exit. (This could be an event structure if you like.)

Clicking the "Load" Button loads all of the COCs from disk into the correct Editor's Tabs.

Yes, all the COCs data files load in one hit, using the Path COC to select the correct file.

The first state loaded is "ADC Setup" and stops loading at "Review data" state, all 13 COC files. The loading converts flattened data to the original COC, using local variables for each COC as "Type" or Shape.

The Paths for each COC file are unbundled and selected as the State Engine runs through the 13 files, as seen in the next pict.

When completed the Editor goes back to the "Idle" state.

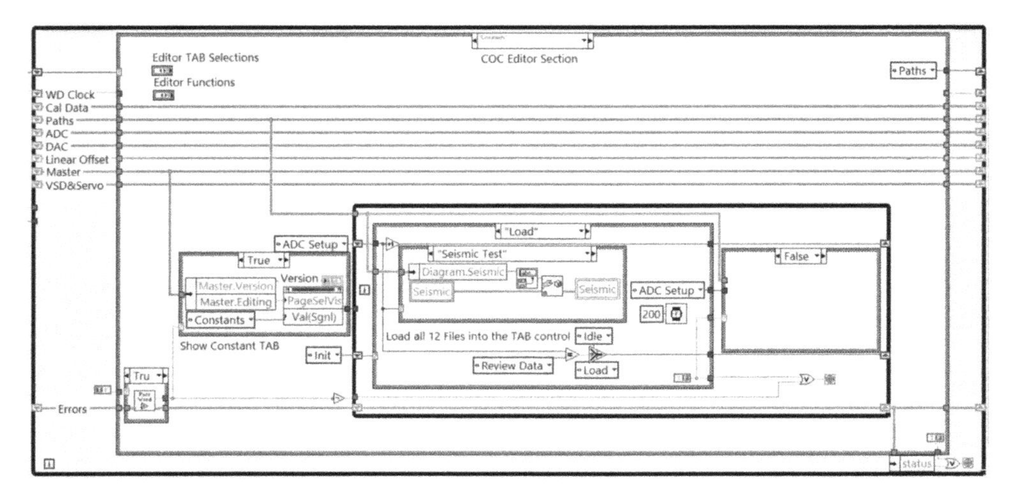

Top The COC editor's Load state

The "Save" Button just saves the Editor's current selected and displayed Tab COC data to disk. Just one COC each time the "Save" Button is clicked.

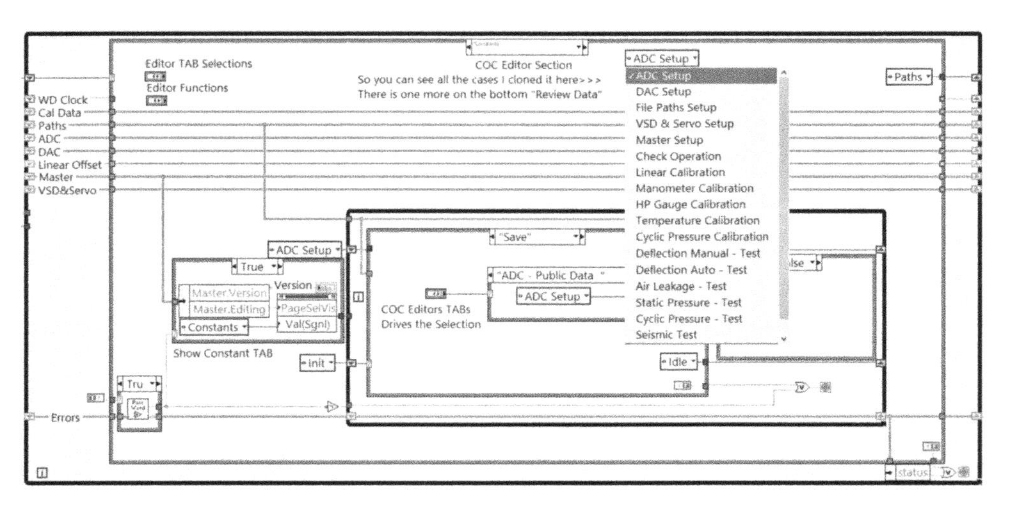

The COC editor's Save state

The selection of which COC is saved is decided by which COC is displayed.

If you are displaying and editing the “ADC” Tab, then the Save button will only save that “ADC” COC to file. The Save All button saves all the Editor’s Tabs with COC, using Paths again to direct the 13 Files.

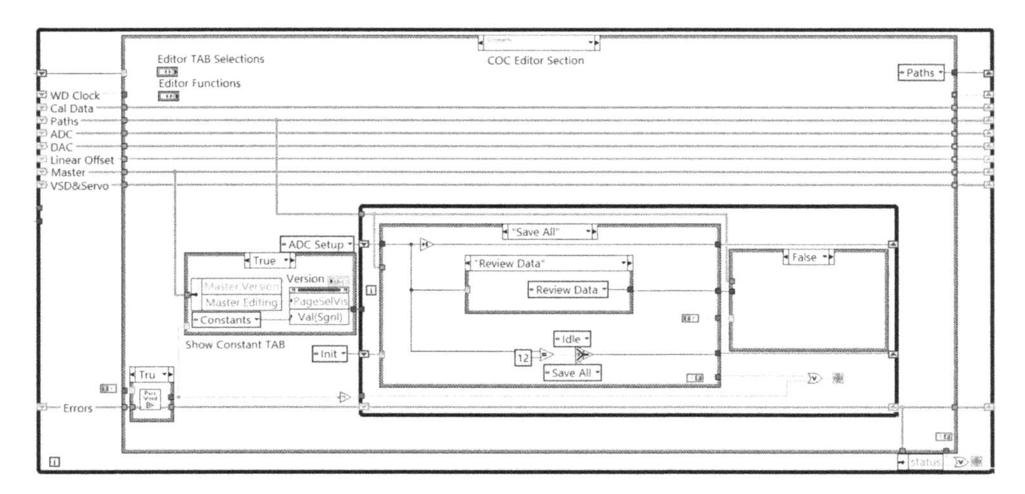

The COC editor’s Save All state

The Exit button puts the State Engine into Exit mode.

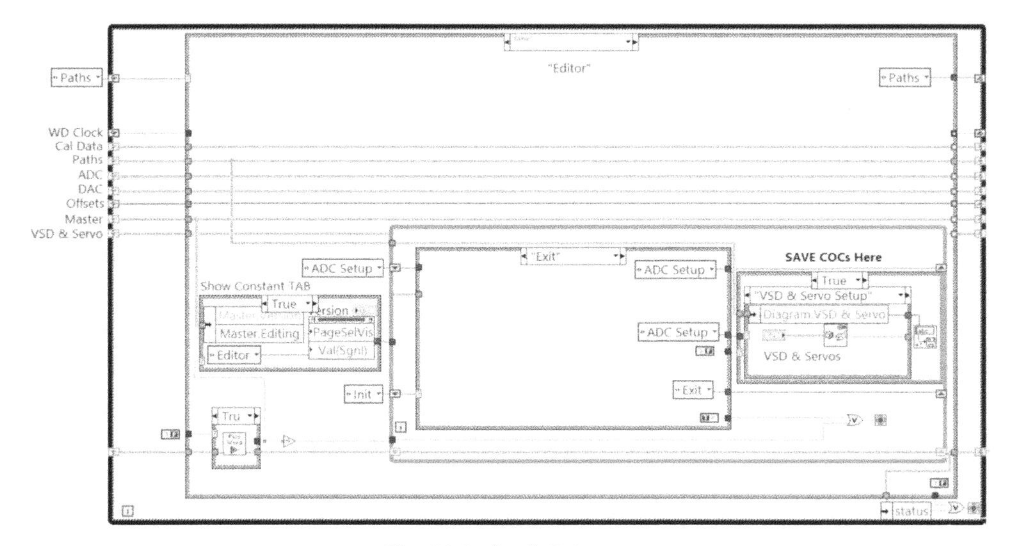

The COC editor’s Exit state

Notice that on exiting the Editor, the State Engine sets the Main Application diagram Case or State Selector's right SR to Paths.

This is to restart or reboot the Main Program at the Path's case (the first case or state in the Main program). This process reloads all the loaded and edited COCs data back to the SRs from disk again. The program is now refreshed with new edited public COCs data and ready to go.

Also, all the Private Data COC are on file edited and ready to go but not loaded until their respective SubVIs run.

Using the Editor

Just to recap.

Now to walk through using this Editor.

Bring up the Editor by clicking the button "Show constants".

This displays the main Front Panel Tab with the embedded Tab control with all the program's COC Tabs.

To Load all the COC with data from disk file, the operator clicks the "Load" button.

To Save the selected and displayed COC (just one COC) with edited data to disk file, the operator clicks the "Save" button.

To Save All the COC with edited data to disk file, the operator clicks the "Save All" button.

So that is the Simple Editor, just a state engine using the Tab control to select and display the COC on the Tabs and four buttons to drive a 13-step State Engine, using the enum Type Def Constants (verbs).

Notice the enum Type Defs verbs for driving and controlling the States.

These enums give the Cases names rather than a number. Meaningful. Abstraction again.

Now the Editor is built, run it up and save all those Type Def COC to file.

Yes, all those COCs in the Editor's Tabs are to be made into Type Defs.

The reason of course is that these same COCs are scattered throughout the program on SubVI's Front Panels also.

These scattered Type Def COCs will auto update if while developing you change the shape of any COCs by adding or subtracting constants in any of the COCs.

Note: If when you are developing and do add or subtract a constant to a Type Def COC and save it, you will see your PC hesitate while it does the big rebuild throughout the whole program of all the COC linked to that Edit.

Note: almost every major SubVI in my programs have the Tabs with COCs in them.

Then load them back and check the data to see if the read was correct. It will be.

As you are building the Editor, don't fret if the Save was bad because of a diagram mistake. You have the Type Def COC with the default values set so that you can bring them back for another shot at saving.

So that is Question 5 complete.

But it is not the end of the story of course, as there's just a little more to round it out and that is how to put this saved COC data back into a diagram in an orderly manner.

Let's look at that.

CHAPTER 13
LOADING PUBLIC CLUSTER CONSTANTS ONTO SHIFT REGISTERS

Focus: How to incorporate the Public Data Clusters back into the Main Program.

I did a lot of work with these little computers. I used them as terminals for our HP RTE 1000 Mini.

The Apple II machines were easy to repair, as they had loads of socketed TTL chips in them. No ASICs in the II.

When I was running CPM multitasking Z80 Forth in a II, I could plot up to 1000 pts/sec on a graph. Not too bad for a little 8-bit banger.

Apple II — Wozniak's baby

HOW TO INCORPORATE THE PUBLIC DATA CLUSTERS BACK INTO THE MAIN PROGRAM

Loading the Public COC from file at run time

This is a reiteration of previous sections but shows the complete loading of COCs.

In the "Main" diagram, I always load all the public COCs first.

The "Main" diagram is a State Engine with several "Initialisation" states for loading COCs.

After each load of a public COC from file, I put the COC data onto one of the right-hand shift registers on the Main Program's While Loop, as has been shown throughout the discussion.

These steps make those COC Data public, available to all parts of the program and SubVIs.

The next diagram shows the first state called "Paths" where the Paths for all files for the program are loaded onto an SR.

The whole program revolves around this loading of paths and the COC data being placed on the shift registers.

Starting this process is of interest and is the heart of success.

This first state to load "Paths" can happen two ways, as follows.

1. Load Paths using a File Path from a file Path constant

This first way is hardwired to a constant and is sort of like the "cold bootstrap loader", from the old days. This uses a Path constant that you type into on the Front Panel.

Notice the "Type" for the Unbundle is a Type Def local variable popped off the Editor's Tab "Paths".

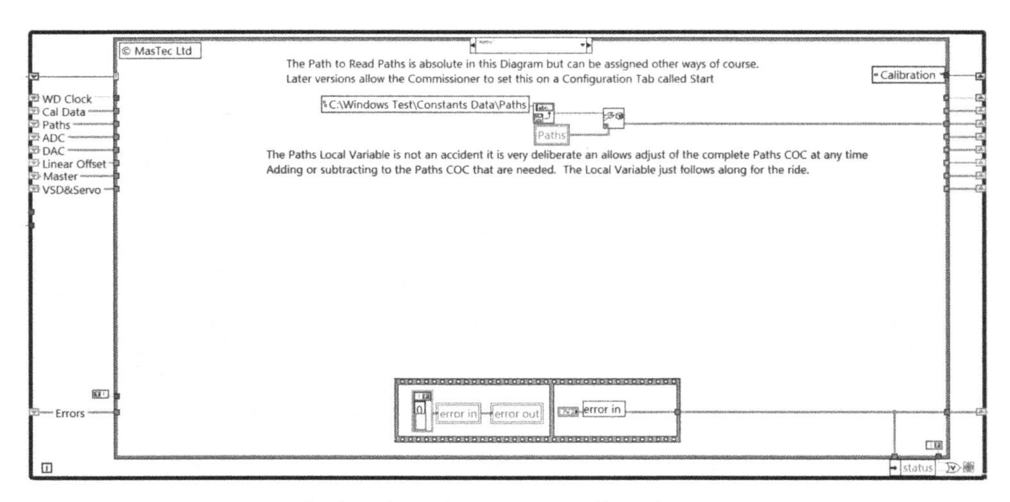

Top loading the Path COC, using a file Path constant

2. Load Paths from the Editor's Tab using the COC stored Path's file "path".

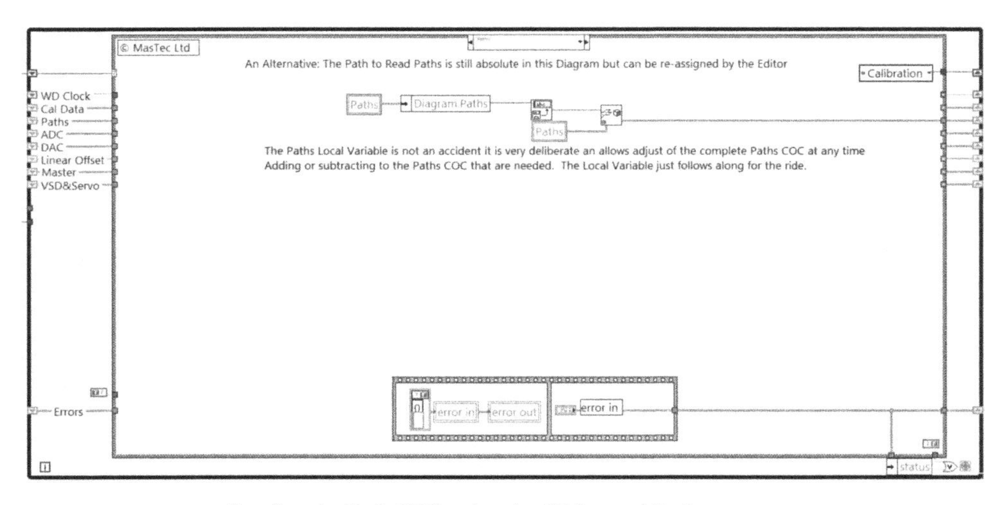

Loading the Path COC, using the COC stored Path constant

This second alternative method is a better way. As there is already a Path local variable in the diagram, use it also to get the Path information to load the Paths COC File.

This method allows editing the Path's Path, without touching the diagram code.

Just use an external Editor to change the Path's COC Path before starting the program.

Note: You can't do it inside the Application because the program will not come up correctly if the first state reading "Paths" is incorrect. In some examples, I offer both ways to load Paths.

So do build a standalone external editor. Just cut and paste one up.

Back to Loading "Paths". "Paths" is now on the Paths SR.

The next State is load COC file for "ADC" and then several more: loading the public COC to the right-hand shift registers one after another. The specific Path for loading all these COC files comes from the first load of the "Paths" COC, just unbundle them off the "Paths" wire.

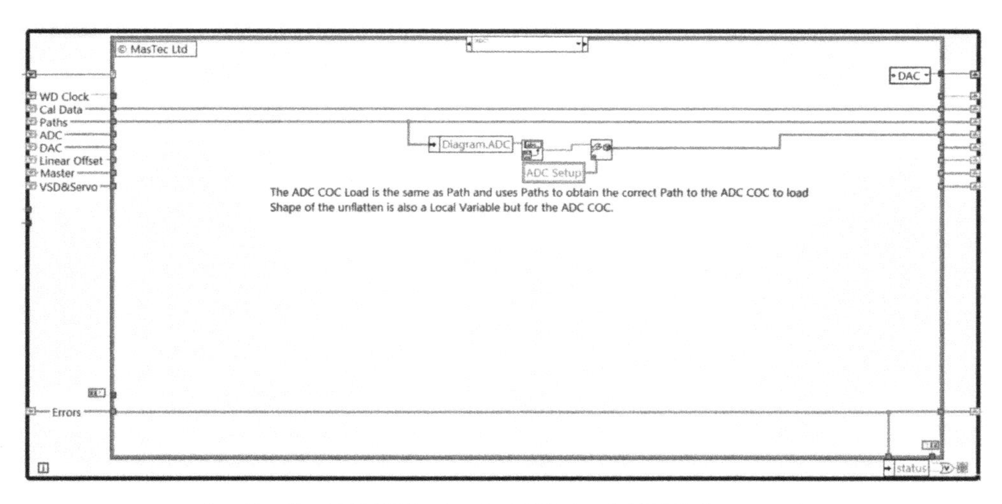

Loading the ADC COC using the COC stored ADC Path constant

When the Initialisation is complete, the "Main" default Front Panel is re-displayed and waits in an "Idle" state for the operator to select a button.

When one of the Front Panel Buttons is selected the program branches to the new selected State.

When the Main Front Panel Button “Show Test” is clicked, this is the State that runs and displays the Tab “Testing”.

This Testing Tab now becomes the FP for the Application with operator buttons to select from.

Select sections for Check, Calibrate, Test or Review.

“Check” allow individual running of the site hardware.

“Calibrate” is an in-depth calibration suite for each sensor.

“Test” has many certified Tests available.

“Review” open and display any test ever done by the rig.

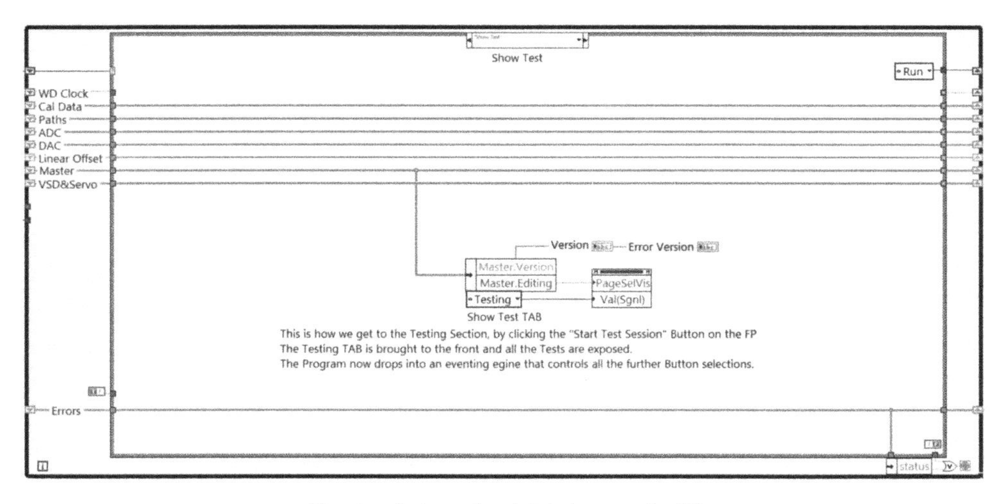

How to select another tab to become the FP

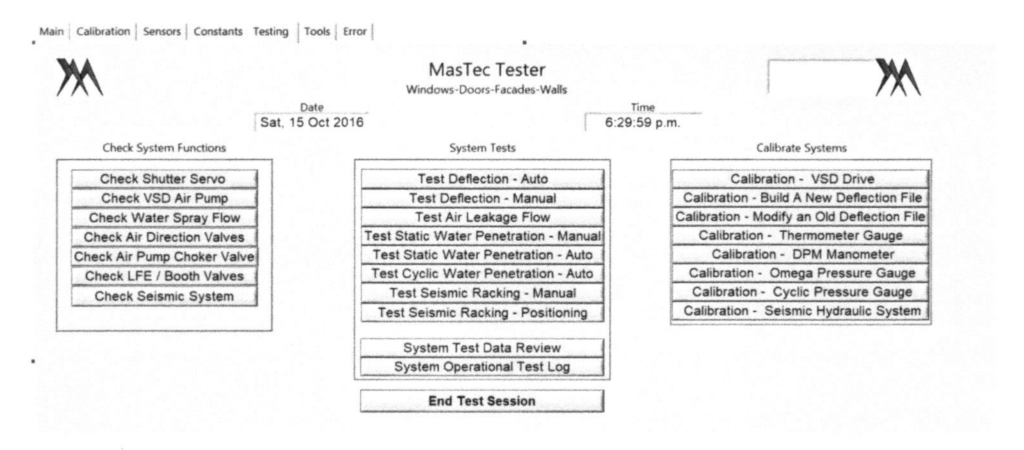

The new FP in the tabs is displayed with a button click

The “End Test Session” button restarts the Main State Engine and goes back to the “Idle State”.

Note: the pic above has no Tabs.

This was achieved by using the Editor to set the Master COC constants switch for Tabs to Off.

See the previous pic of the same front panel with Tabs.

PROGRAM DESIGN COMPLETE

That’s about it for the new “hidden data” method.

We have achieved our original five-question goal:

1. How can we remove *all and any types* of LabVIEW constants out of the diagram?
2. How can we remove those constants out of the program to file in a disk storage system?
3. How can we recover those constants from the file storage system back into the diagram?

4. How can we reinstall the constants into the diagram at load or run time or any time?
5. How can we make an online and offline editor to edit all those removed constants?

All done.

All "constants" are now safely off program on disk and loaded at run time or when needed.

We have a simple in-built Editor and an external editor available to adjust any and all COCs.

We have a "hidden data" or "constants Removal System" that now also allows any LabVIEW Graphical Constants to be used in diagrams and edited off disk, a major step.

Actually "hidden data" in LabVIEW is very limited if you cannot use Graphical Constants.

Also, using the Tab Design method to place the COCs, results in an overall improved program design that is simple, flexible, expandable and hideable.

When the program is running in "user mode" rather than "development mode", all the Tabs are hidden nicely away and no one is even aware of what resides in the other Tab panels or even know there are other Tabs.

And, of course, this program is now configurable remotely also by two methods:

1. Using something like Teamviewer to get into sites and remotely drive the program up to "development mode" and change any of the COCs with the Editor, *or*
2. The developer has a master copy of the COC files and can edit them remotely and reload the files to the remote Test system to affect the change required.

THE WRAP-UP

Just a few more helpful tips to expose and we can all sign off and get on with our lives.

Reusing

After you have built one of these hidden data applications, you can use it as a very large template for your next program.

Reuse all the pieces.

When developing

Always reuse the first SubVIs developed. These already have a full COC Tab set of Type Def COCs, as a template to clone from. It will save a heap of extra work. This allows you almost to have the Front Panel Tabs complete; just make the Applications Main Front Panel.

Reuse of the State Engines and the Editor

Next, build and edit those already-built SubVIs with (Type Def COCs) what is required in the new program, and the new application will emerge very quickly.

More refinements: adding Tabs to the main Front Panel

- More Main Panel Tabs for more functionality access. Note: This does not always have to be for placing COC in. Add a Tab if you need more functionality.
- Examples Tabs for Errors, Warnings etc.
- Another Tab for Installation Tools. In this SubVI set, I have Spectrum Analyser, DVM, Scope, and Noise Measurement software tools as individual SubVIs instruments.
- Also add a Tab for “Messages”, a msg system for each test that instructs the operator what to do.

- And lastly, a Tab for "Troubleshoot", similar to Message but only the commissioning engineer has access. It goes right down to DVM work on signals, which wire, which terminal etc.

The next pic shows some of these additions. Notice the new Tabs Tools, Warnings, Errors.

I also use passwords to allow access to the Editor, Installation Tools and Trouble Shooting.

I also included on the front main page a heartbeat LED so the operator knows the TCP DAQ is running. The heartbeat is linked around a TCP DAQ VI that has to run to make the LED run.

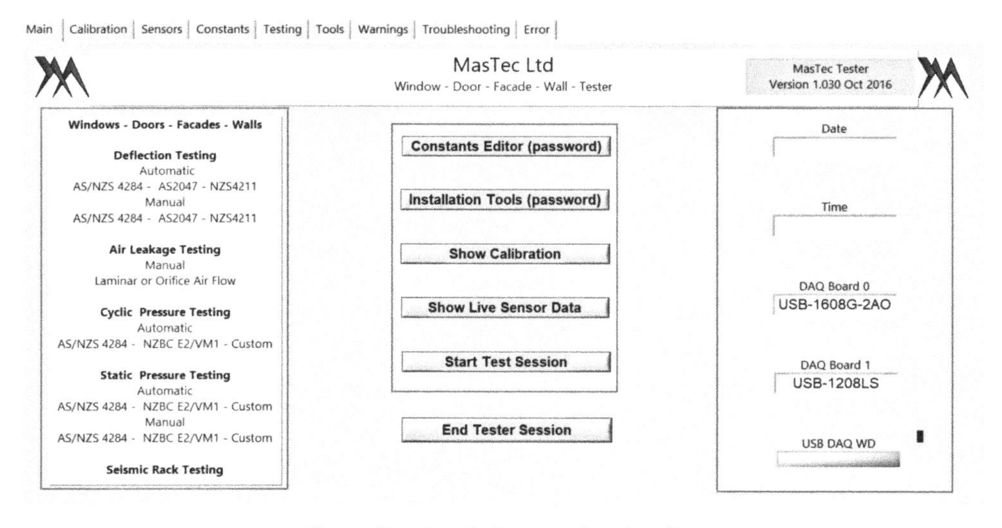

Expanding the tabs for more functionality

You can see this tidies up old messes quite well and makes for a more thorough design.

Improving diagram documentation further

We can improve the look and documentation inside the diagram a little further.

In the original COC, you can add a few extra little details to make things even more clear, leading to better automatic documentation.

When starting the hidden data de-constant process, build a main cluster and now add several more sub-clusters inside the Main cluster and name these sub-clusters according to the state the constants are coming from. These become sort of like Instances of the COC classes.

When you convert these COC constants, the result produces even more meaningful documentation in the unbundle terminal labels.

Example

This pic is a COC for a SubVI named “Deflection Testing Manual”.

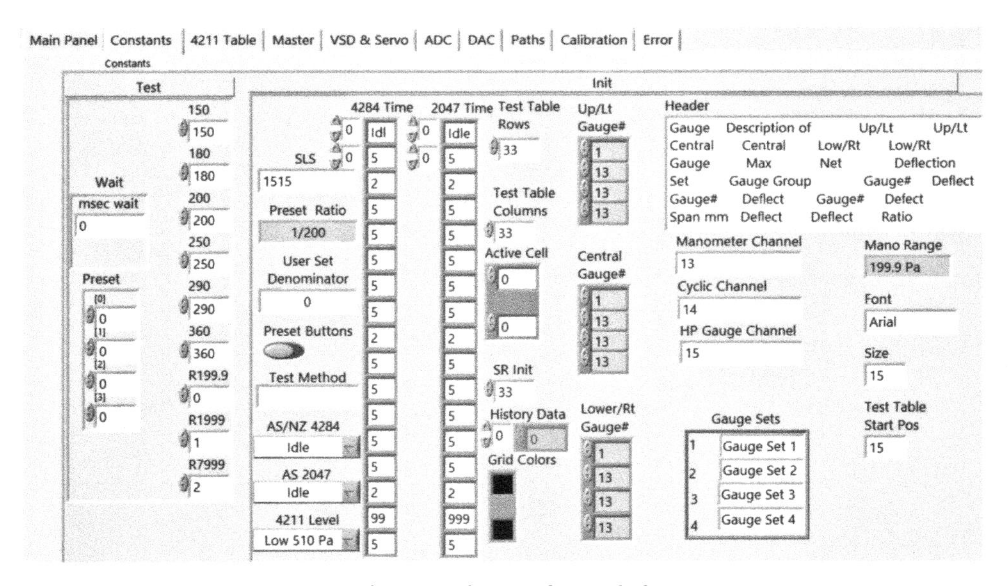

Expanding COC design to have sub clusters

In this example, the main COC has two clusters inside with COC data. Each cluster is unbundled in its state and used.

There are two clusters inside the Main Cluster named “constants”: sub-cluster “Init” and “Test”.

Naming them is the important part. Use the same name as the State that the constants are in.

Notice in the next two pics that when the unbundling takes place, the State name is in the prefix to the name of the constant.

In the “Init” state the constants unbundle terminal labels are now prefixed with “Init” etc.

A nice little addition.

The “Test” State Constant Unbundle terminal labels are now prefixed with “Test”. So these are just a couple of little helpful things. You can dream up your own.

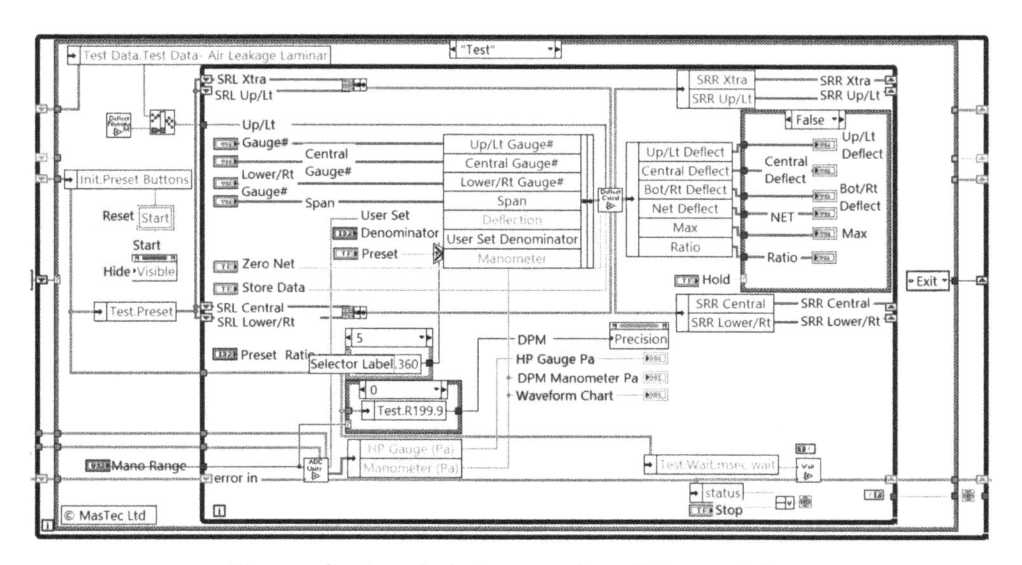

Diagram showing sub-clusters expanding self-documentation

Just to show it off further, you can take this as far as you like.

Add a sub sub COC in the “Test” sub COC called “Wait”.

Note this sub-cluster “Wait” is in the “Test” COC state.

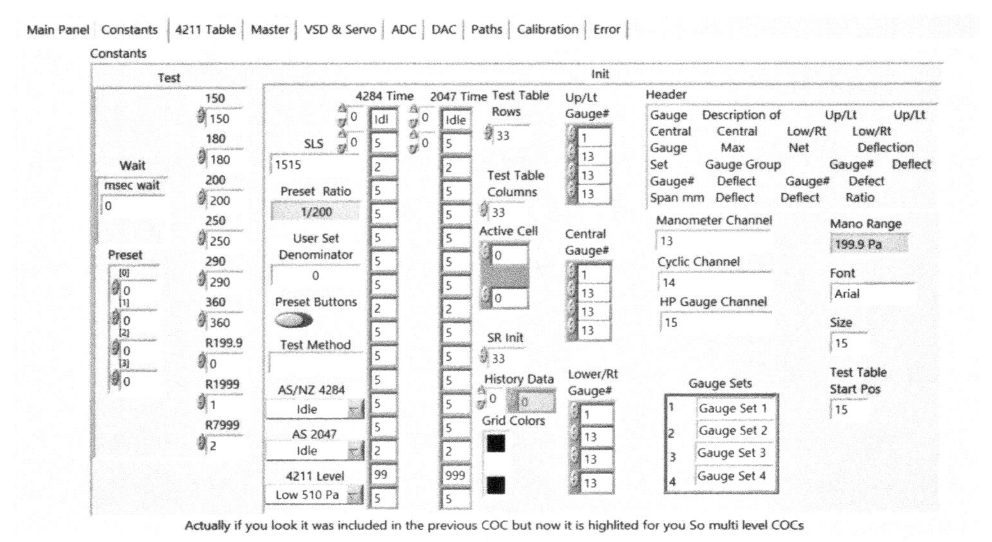

Additional sub-clusters naming for self-documentation

SOME MORE WRAP-UP

Master Cluster

I promised earlier to show a bigger Master COC for the new Universal Tester Version using the TCP Modbus DAQ distributed modules.

In the Tab Master, the displayed panel has several clusters of COCs to allow setting up the new Universal Program. These COCs are used to configure the application for what hardware is present for this site or tests. These COCs data are also used at run time.

Notice you can even set up to run with no I/O, which is helpful when developing with no hardware to allow creating the look and feel of the Front Panels.

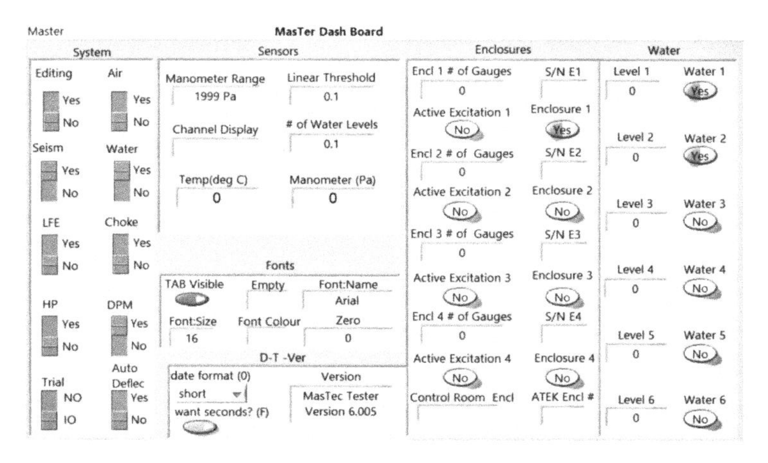

The master COC expanded to allow global configurations

The next pic shows how the settings in the "Master" Tab tumble out in the "Test Panel" when the Application actually runs.

The greyed-out buttons mean that functionality and/or I/O are not available according to the Master COCs set-up.

This is very helpful.

Here's an example. The DPM manometer gauge is a way to get calibrated and verified. In Master COC set the DPM switch to No. The program will automatically use the other differential airflow gauge in all the tests.

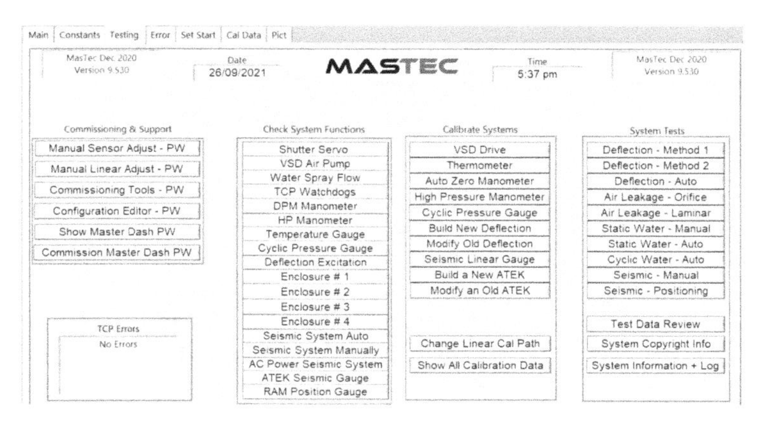

The master COC controls which FP buttons become active

That is enough on hidden data using this new LCOD method. You can keep expanding it as you will.

Every time I program, I add more into the applications; it is so quick and easy.

This new Universal TCP Application will work at disparate sites because of the "Master" COC settings.

Some of the Test sites are simple, some are complex and they have all the technology. Using that new style of "Master" Tab, I can quickly set up for any site's hardware and layout. This means I only have to have one application to run a dozen different levels of technology sites. In the past, they all had individual applications, and it was a big job to keep them all current.

Hope you enjoyed that last little piece, it is very useful and powerful.

Next, we'll look at Abstraction in the next chapter.

Some very interesting stuff in this chapter.

CHAPTER 14
ABSTRACTION

IBM PC Junior XT 1983 with ISA XT 8-bit Bus

Focus: How to build Components with Abstraction Levels.

The IBM PC was a marketing opportunity that NI took very early. NI released an 8-bit ISA GPIB card. I think the PCIIA?

Up until that time HP had the GPIB market cornered since they had invented this technology.

Before the PC, most of NI's GPIB efforts were focused on minis, especially DEC minicomputers.

I purchased one of these cards in 1979, a DEC LSI-11 GPIB board for linking up to my HP and other instruments.

IBM really launched NI into GPIB Interface cards and software in a big way.

NI received a big order from IBM for the new ISA GPIB Cards.

The story that I heard, goes somewhat like this: right from the horses mouth.

This young NI external sales guy who had the sales route of most of the US's east coast happened to be visiting IBM Raleigh in North Carolina.

A large GPIB order was handed to him on that visit. All previous visits apparently were empty.

He got back to his car opened the order and freaked out and drove all the way to NI Texas to deliver it. He was a hero that day.

Next day, IBM rang and said they had made a terrible mistake, and doubled the order.

I love that story. A lot of beer, singing and dancing that day.

"ABSTRACTION" — ANOTHER FOCUS OF THE BOOK

Abstraction is used in thinking, planning, designing and explaining in all things.

We abstract naturally every day, just living and communicating with one another and to ourselves.

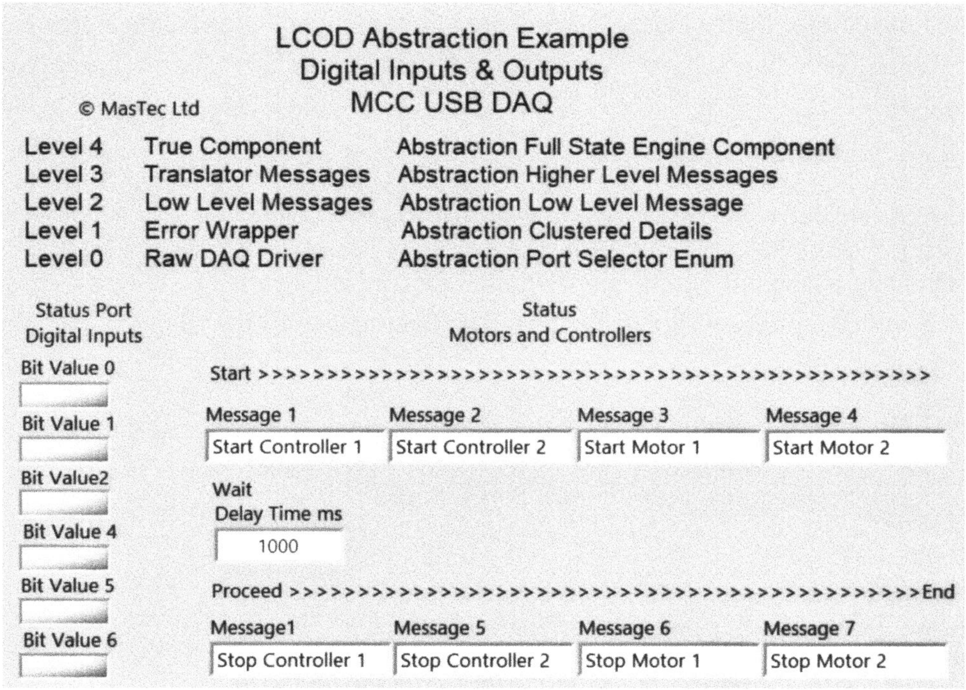

Abstraction example FP

If you met a person who is not a programmer and you start telling them what you are programming and how, you will quickly have to start abstracting the language with them so they can understand. Probably several layers of abstraction or give up!

Abstracting is the inherent purpose of any computer programming language. Assemblers move ideas from machine-level binary or hex code to text language mnemonics with characters and numbers.

Forth, Basic, C Code etc abstract ideas from mnemonics to language words with higher-level meaning words for math, logic and control.

Higher-level programming languages just create higher-level abstractions/descriptions of the same idea. Hopefully.

The purpose of the LabVIEW Front Panel is abstraction, to allow the operator to work in a language they understand, and to allow them to drive the program with high-level visual selections and engineering units (or their particular discipline's units).

The purpose of LabVIEW diagram abstraction is two-fold:

Primarily to make higher-level diagrams that make it easier to program and also understandable later. LabVIEW with abstraction in the diagram can be very good at this.

Secondly to move the low-level computer language and function details down into hidden lower levels of the diagrams, creating several hierarchical levels of abstraction, ideas and functionality not seen at first glance but that can be opened if need be.

The inherent development methods and tools for LabVIEW naturally abstract.

Front Panels:

Abstraction is inherent in all Front Panels by presenting to the operator adjustable visual tokens that are recognised and known and understood in their discipline. (the fateful slider)

Diagrams:

The icons and structures in a diagram are an immediate visual abstraction.

With LCOD components icons are also an abstraction.

Also the high-level language messages sent to any component are converted down into lower-level computer languages or ideas for execution. A true abstraction sometimes of several layers.

The high-level "Message" is a verb, and this directs the action of the states in the "Component" engine (Noun).

Next we will look at several examples of abstraction, starting at lower levels and working up to somewhat higher levels.

The last and highest abstraction level will show off a new way to abstract that maybe you have never seen before.

Abstraction Levels

The large diagram shows a series of Abstraction Levels and or Methods.

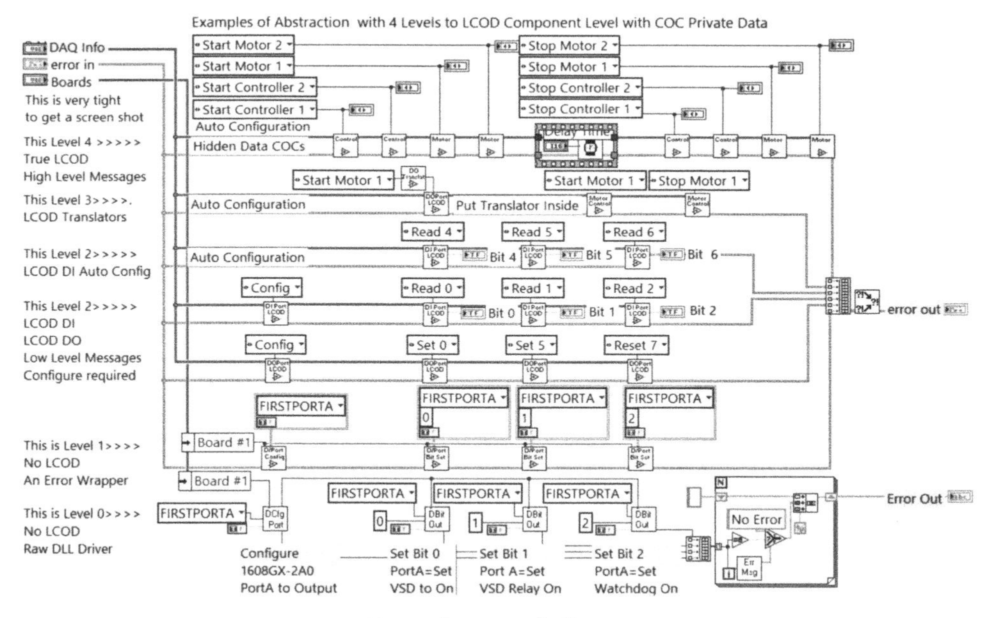

Abstraction example diagram

The five abstraction levels, top to bottom:

Level 4 High Level Message Component — Best LCOD >> Abstraction, COC and much more

Level 3 High Level Message Wrapper — Closer LCOD >> Abstracted, One Component

Level 3 High Level Message Wrapper — Close LCOD >> Abstracted, High Level Messages

Level 2 Low Level Message Wrapper — Almost LCOD >> Abstracted, A better DI Component

Level 2 Low Level Message Wrapper — Almost LCOD >> Abstracted, Start of DO Component

Level 1 Error Wrapper around Level 0 — No LCOD >> Abstracted, Hides the LV Driver

Level 0 Raw DAQ LV Driver — No LCOD >> Abstracted, Better than C Code

Level 0 Abstraction

Level 0 >> Raw LV functions >> configure and setting bits in a selected digital parallel port.

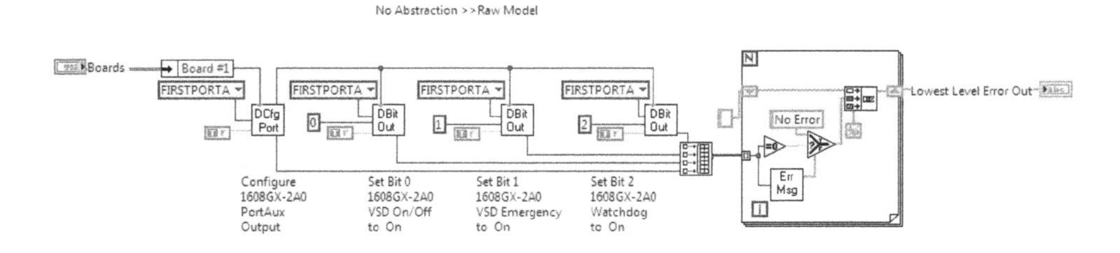

Level 0 (raw) abstraction example diagram

This example uses the MCCDAQ Legacy LV Driver VIs:

Two SubVIs used: Configure the digital port and set that digital output port's bits individually.

This Abstraction level >> easier to read than Hex, Mnemonics or C Code.

Also hides most of the computer parallel port technical details.

The MCC DAQ driver is actually a “LV graphical wrapper” around their own C code driver DLL.

In fact, if you think about this a little more, LabVIEW Icons are in general all “Graphical wrapper abstractions” that have hidden inside them at their lowest level, computer executable code.

That is one of the reasons we like LabVIEW so much, as the front panels, the icons and the diagrams abstractions hide most of the computer detail and allows development at a more human concepts, ideas and symbols abstraction development.

This Level 0 snippet configures any of MCCDAQ digital parallel port modules. This can be many different multifunction DAQ or plain vanilla digital IO modules. They can be ISA, PCI, PCIe, USB or TCP interfaces. It allows using the same programming across all devices.

This example sets up and controls “FIRSTPORTA” as an 8-bit parallel output port and then proceeds to set bits 0, 1 and 2 to True.

Individual errors for each of the SubVIs are captured and reported.

Note this MCCDAQ driver VIs do not make error term driven data dependency execution available but the Configuration VI always runs first and generates some data dependency using the Board # which propagates after the configuration of the port.

Those enum constants in the diagram pop from the MCCDAQ LV driver and allow selection of the available digital ports.

The MCC DAQ programmers of this LV driver did the first level of abstraction over their own abstracting C code DLL.

Level 1 Abstraction

Level 1 >> Wrapper >> Error terminals In and Out allows for data dependency execution

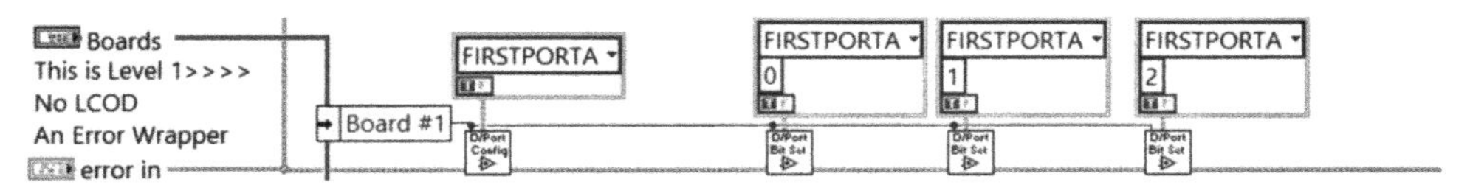

Level 1 abstraction wrapper example diagram

Example using a more sophisticated LV wrapper around the MCCDAQ LV driver VIs:

The Digital Output Port Configure VI

The abstraction cluster "controls" contains the port number and the port direction input data.

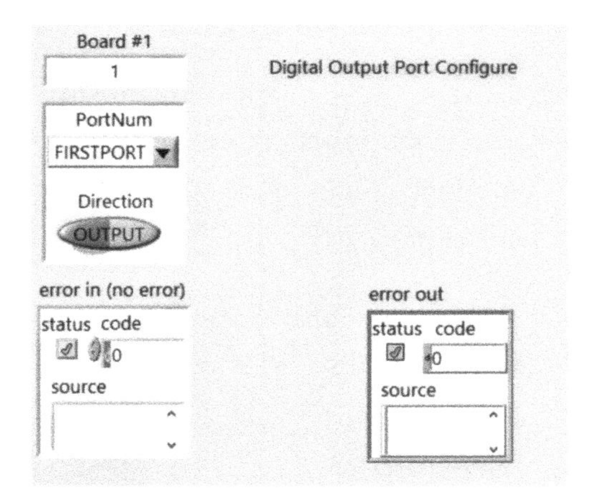

Level 1 abstraction wrapper example configuration FP

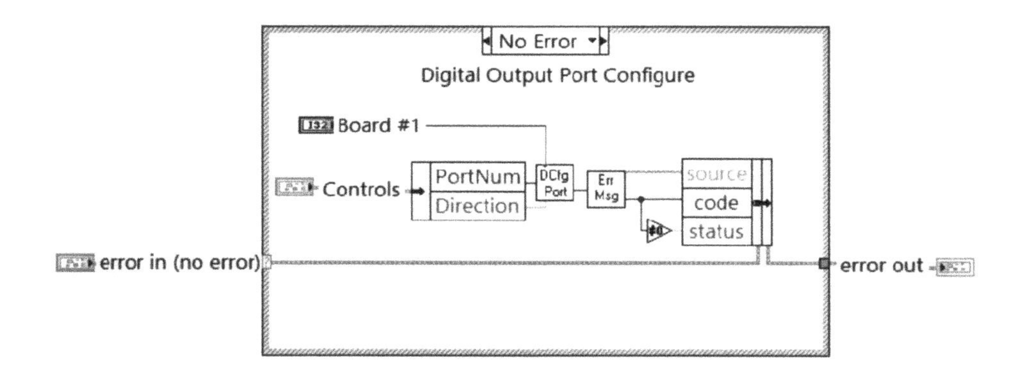

Level 1 abstraction wrapper internals example configuration diagram

The Digital Output Bit Set VI

The first cluster "controls" contains the port number, bit # and the bit value setting.

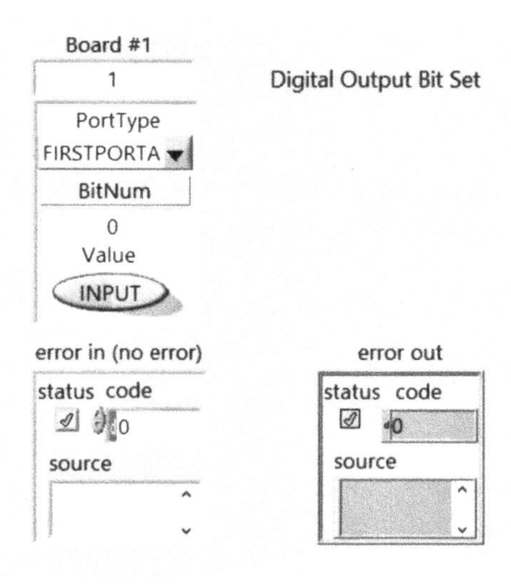

Level 1 abstraction wrapper example output FP

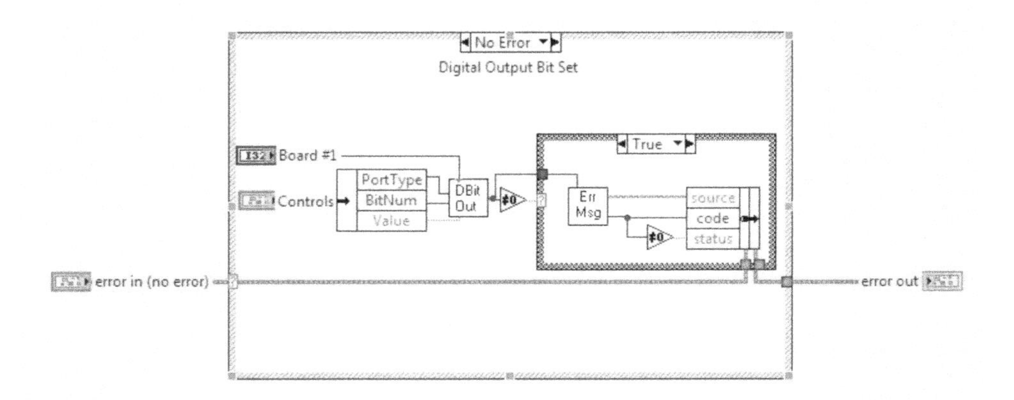

Level 1 abstraction wrapper internals example output diagram

Note that all of these LV SubVI diagrams are in a no error/error case, for fail-through on entry error. I always try to use this fail-through method, as errors quickly propagate through a program with nothing else executing after the error and then offer the error to the operator in some way.

You can trap the error and try and fix things if you are clever or at least tell the operator what is going on.

Abstract the note to the operator so they know what was error # 14987476 actually means the USB cable is not plugged in.

Level 2 Abstraction Digital Outputs

Only one Component is now doing all the work and has a new set of higher-level messages.

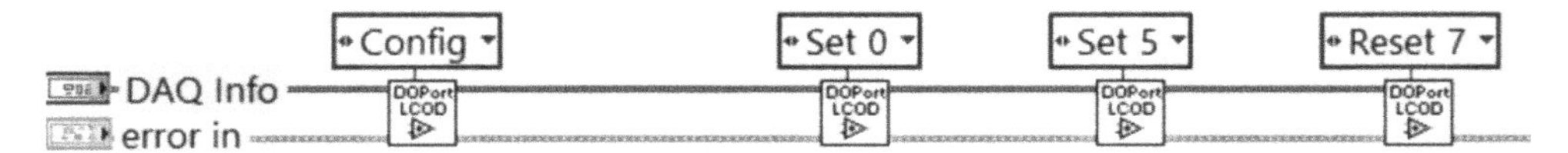

Level 2 abstraction messages example output components

Now we are starting to see improved nouns and verbs.

Also, more hiding of lower-level details.

This is the start of building one Component that does it all with much higher-level messages.

The Messages (verbs) >> Config, Set 0, Set 1, Set 2.

The Component DOPort allows all the design criteria to be met.

The message set used in this abstraction still needs to be elevated to higher abstraction levels.

These messages (verbs) drive the DOPort component.

Notice the port type is now inside a cluster named "DAQ Info". This makes much more sense because if we are using several digital ports, we will want to make the port selection available in a DAQ selection COC.

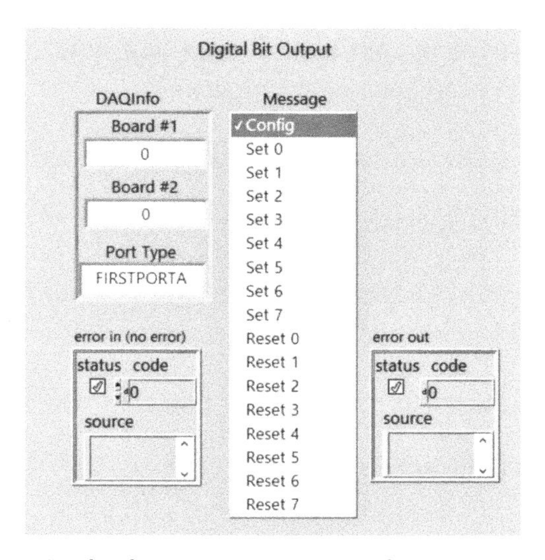

Level 2 abstraction messages example output FP

The diagram for DOPort has only two states, Configuration and Set 0.

By subtracting the current selected verb message's value (from Set 1 to Reset 7) with the value of Set 0 and Reset 0, the actual port bit # to set or reset is calculated.

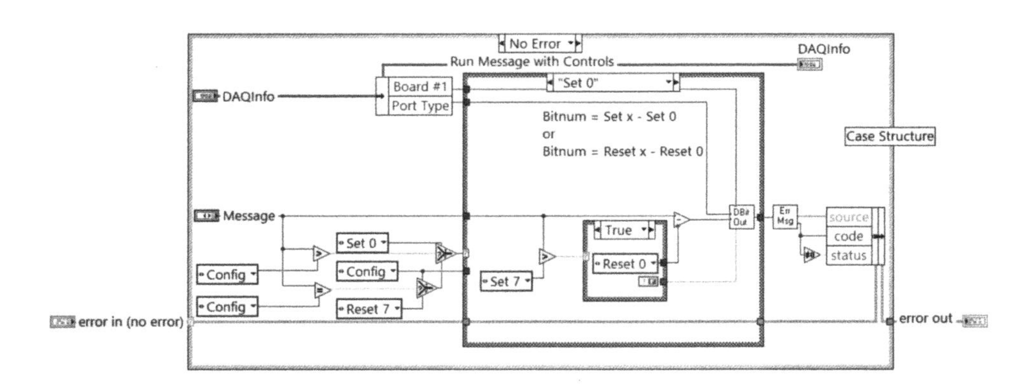

Level 2 abstraction messages example output diagram

This Component can action configuration, set and reset on any of the 8 bits on a digital output port and even report an error.

It also allows and includes error term-driven data-dependent execution.

There are still improvements required.

Note: This Component does have a design fault that allows a set or a reset without first a config state which will cause errors.

However, it does start to show promise for a one-component solution.

Level 2 Abstraction Digital Inputs

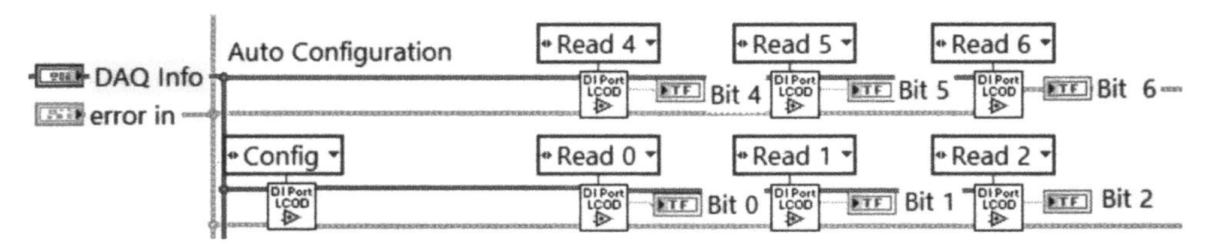

Level 2 abstraction messages example output and input components

Now the Level 2 digital input abstraction.

Very similar to the last example, abstraction Level 2 digital output.

There are two versions of the DIPort VI.

The first version of DIPort, in the lowest line, still requires the configuration message first which leaves the component open to abuse. What happens if we don't send that message first?

The newer version of DIPort, in the top line, now has an auto-configuration built in.

The first time this newer version Component runs it configures the parallel port to be a digital input.

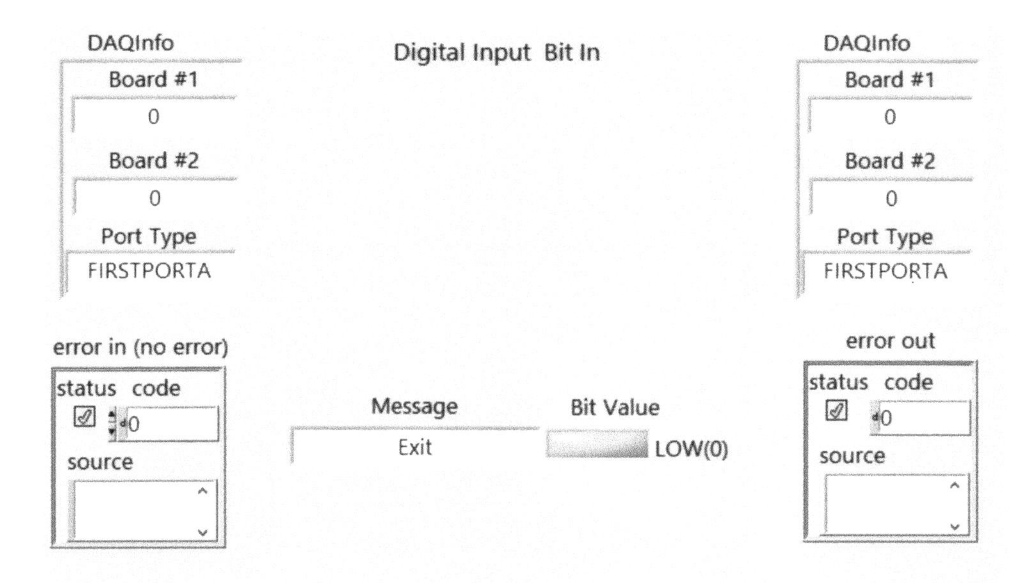

Level 2 abstraction fixing component with auto-configuration

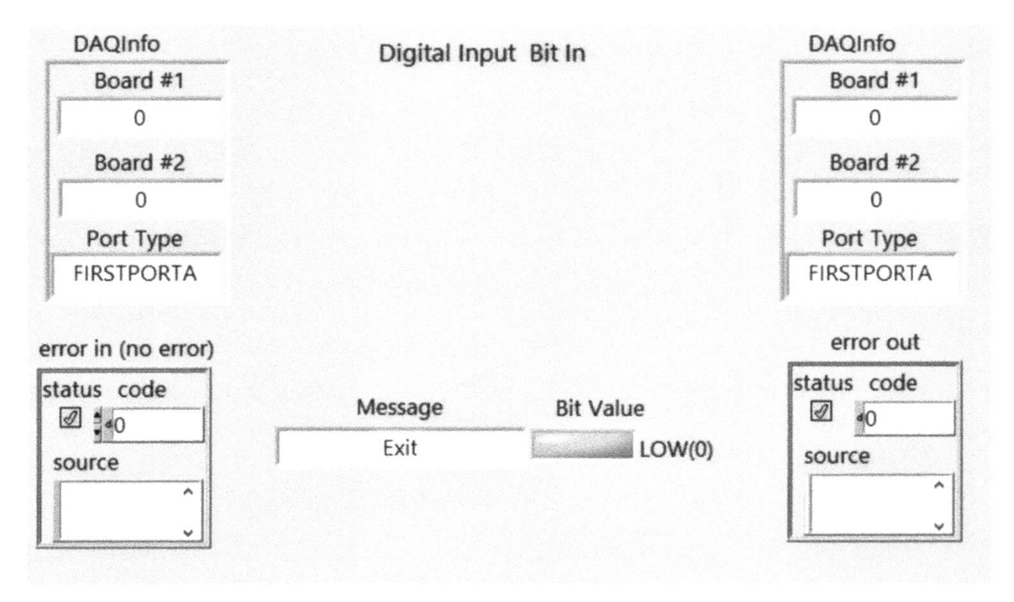

Level 2 abstraction input auto-configuration diagram

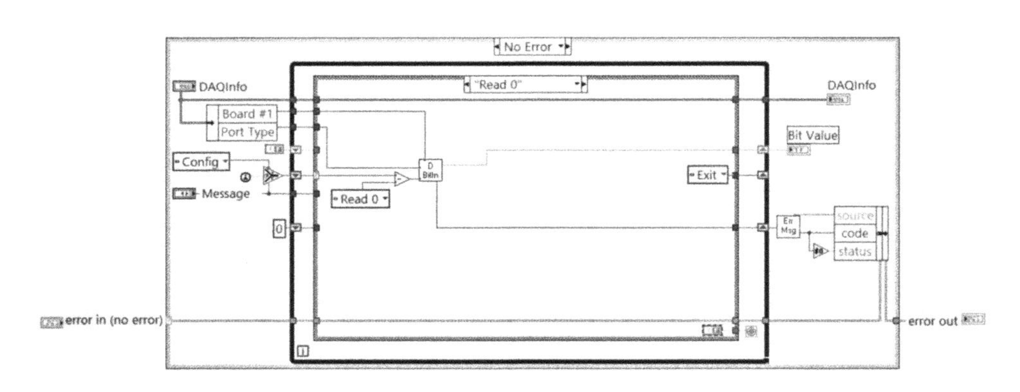

Level 2 abstraction input read diagram with auto-configuration

The "First Call" VI (the little round icon dot with the symbol) forces the message "Config" into the Components state engine on "First Run".

Configuration will even happen if the component's first message it receives is Read x bit on the port.

In this case the state engine Configures the port to input and also then actions the Read Bit State.

Level 3 Abstraction

Making better messages that have "Operator Understood" actions (better verbs).

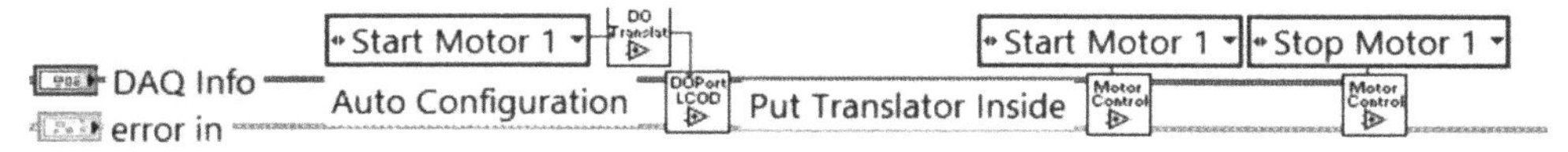

Level 3 abstraction higher level messages

You can just build a Message Translator or a new Verb Builder like the next example.

Make a translator that has a set of high-level messages (or a new set of verbs) and it translates down to the lower-level messages or verbs.

This translator makes messages for use in either of the previous DOPort VIs.

So now we can make high-level messages that describe the "Operator Understood" Actions, like "Start Motor 1".

The Translator takes that high-level message and translates it down to "Set 0" etc.

Very simple.

Looking inside the Translator VI there are no functions in the diagram.

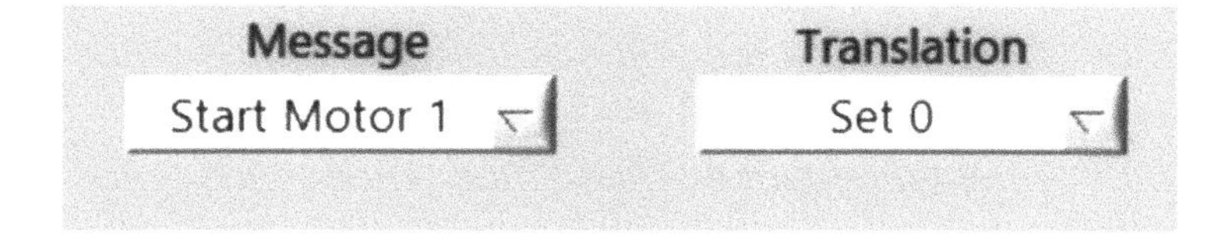

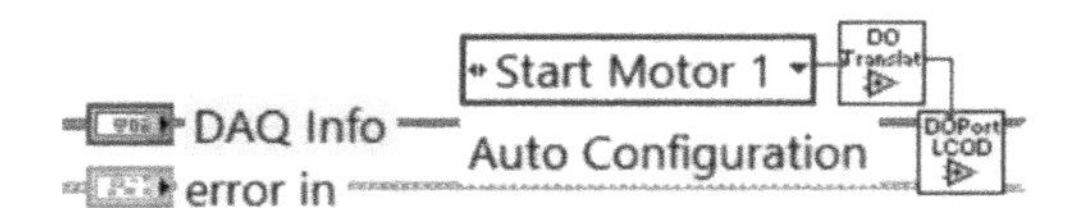

Level 3 abstraction translator component to higher level messages

The control is just wired straight through to the indicator. A direct translation mapping of new verbs or Messages to old verbs or messages.

Start Motor 1 (verb) now = Set 0 (verb).

Only use a Ring on the Indicator, not an enum, or you will get text errors.

The Ring control numerical output drives the message terminal in the DOPort VI.

This method allows abstracting older low-level message Components, to a higher verb set. Just translate or abstract the messages (verbs) up a higher level of language. The other Components in the Level 3 examples have this same translator.

It does look tidier if you put the translation section inside the Component.

U16 Message Translation U16

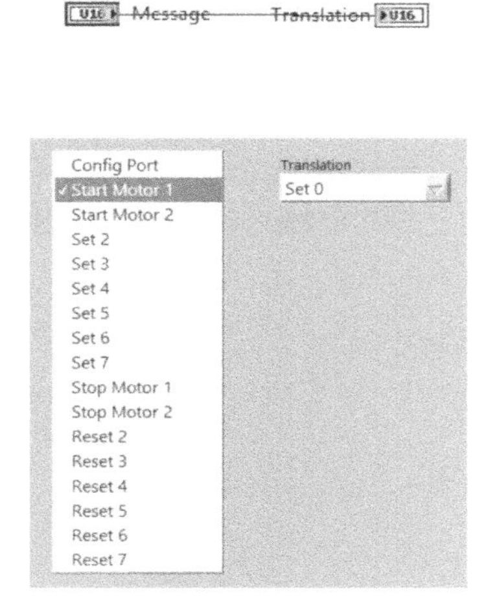

Level 3 abstraction translator FP higher level messages

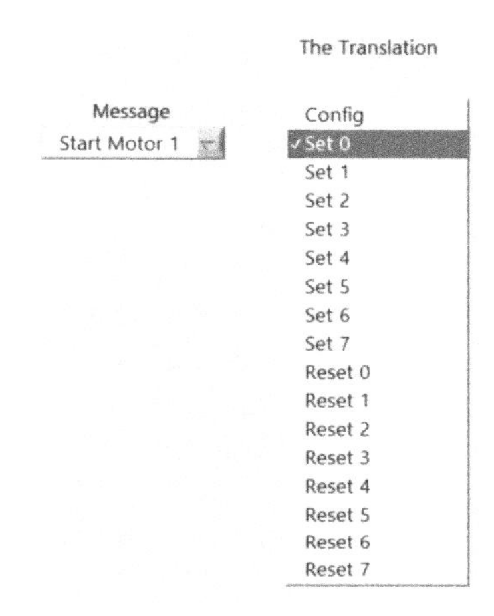

Level 3 abstraction translator FP to lower level messages

Level 3 Components are both Auto Configuration.

This question arises, of course:

Why don't we just make the high-level Messages in the lower-level Components and stop messing around, just do it in one step. Did you think that? Seems reasonable.

The next Level 4 Abstraction below will answer this question in a very powerful way.

Level 4 Abstraction

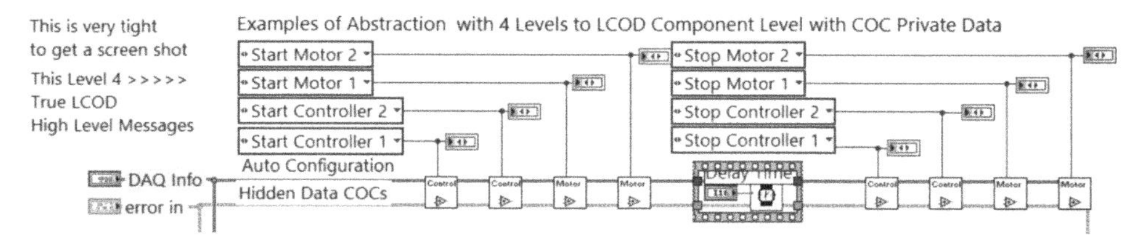

Level 4 LCOD abstraction components wired with high level messages

This has an LCOD Component with high-level Messages plus a private data COC.

Level 4 has two new Components, “Motor” and “Control”.

These Components are basically identical except for their message/verb sets and the names.

Both these Components pop enum constants from their terminals that then allow selecting messages on how the Component will execute.

Notice again the nice diagram abstraction with the enum constants.

These two new Components “Motor” and “Control” are also auto-configuring.

The big addition is that both these Components now have their own COC.

This example will take the original COC idea one step further, introducing a method that will be very handy for future development.

The new types of COCs in this example can now actually determine the execution states, directions and responses for the Component.

In other words, the “Motor” and “Control” Components’ states are directly controlled by their COC settings and are not hardwired.

This method allows external control using the COC disk file settings to control how the diagram’s state engine executes.

Use the COC editor to adjust the COC settings and you can decide how the state engine works.

By having two levels of abstraction in the Component it creates a flexible adjustable state engine method.

The FP shows Tab Main with the first level of abstraction, with the high-level messages.

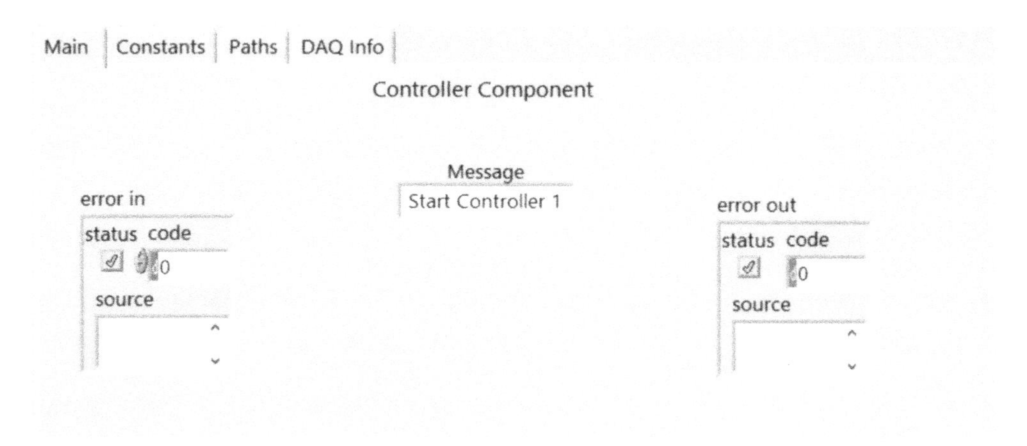

Level 4 LCOD abstraction FP with high level messages

The FP shows Tab constants with the second level of abstraction, with the lower-level messages.

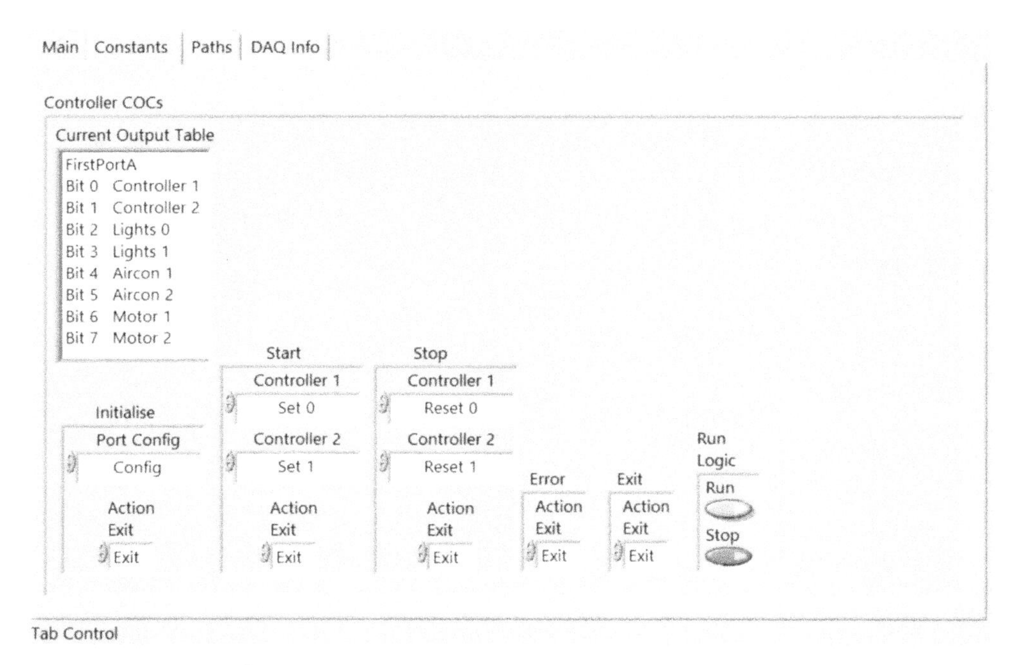

Level 4 LCOD component abstraction with second level abstraction

The COC for the Component "Control" is loaded during the Initialise state from disk like normal.

However, notice in the FP above that this type of COC now has "Type Def message clusters" for each of the Component's states. This was discussed in previous chapters.

At runtime initialisation when the COC's lower-level "message clusters" are unbundled, the state's "actions, execution and exit" rules are set.

Plus of course, the component's primary function is driving the digital output port bit.

The main point to note here about driving the digital port bits is that the selection of the bit # is now decided by the COC state's unbundled cluster settings or values.

The SubVI used for the digital port control is Level 2 DOPort LCOD. We could use any of the DOPort SubVIs from Level 0 Level 1 and the level 2 one used here.

Level 2 DOPort LCOD is the version without the auto-configuration built in. Auto config is not required as the "Control" Component does auto port configuration.

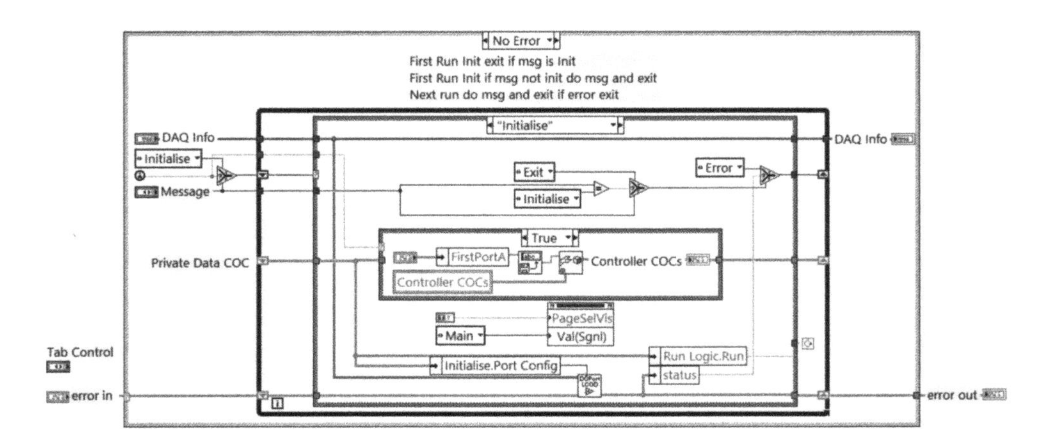

Level 4 LCOD abstraction component diagram initialisation state with COCs

Also, notice the "Start" and "Stop" states in Component Control are nearly identical and the action in these states is decided by these new COCs' states messages and are not programmed in or hardwired.

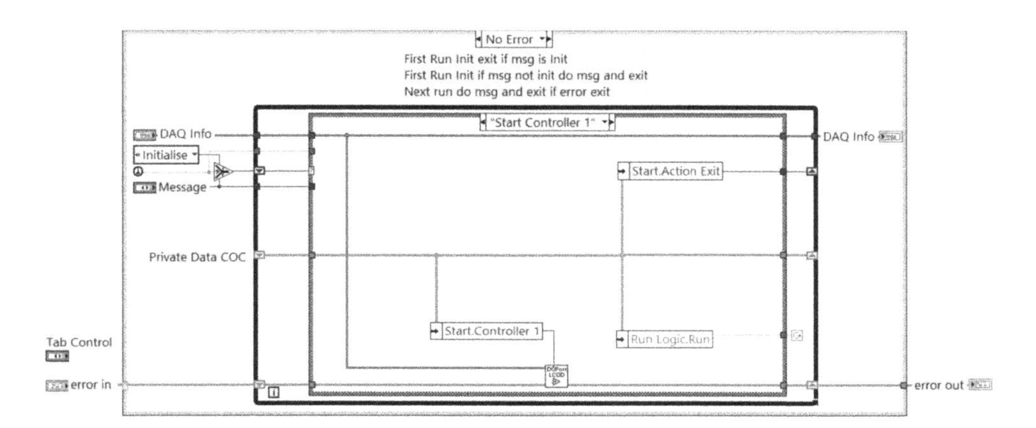

Level 4 LCOD abstraction component start message state

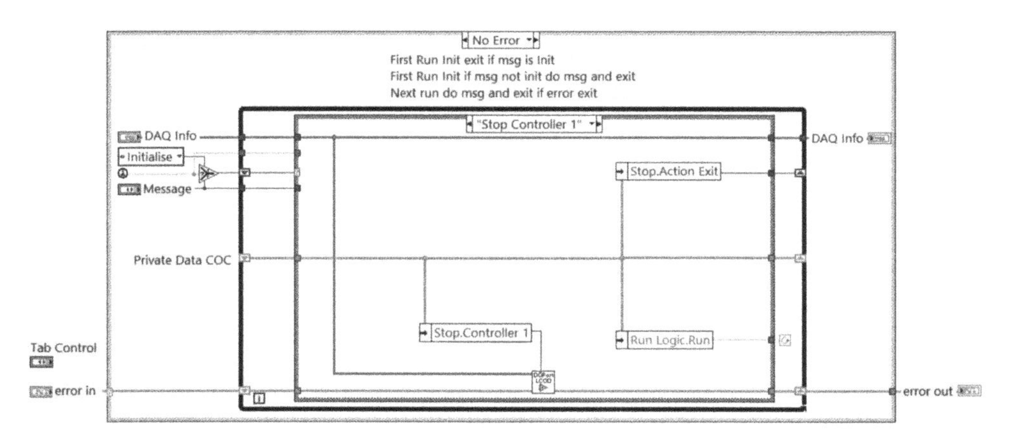

Level 4 LCOD abstraction component stop message state

Now for the "Why the Two Levels of Abstraction?"

The Component "Control's" first abstraction is the high-level messages that are "Operator Understood" words, like "Control 1 On", "Control 1 Off".

However by using two levels of abstraction, now these high-level messages do not decide which digital port bit # is selected and also what state the bit is set to. It is just a message that describes an action that is required. How it is achieved is not these high-level messages' concern any more.

The COC's state clusters settings actually do the deciding of the bit # and the bit state.

In other words, the high-level "Control" message can be "Control 1 ON" but the bit # that that message control uses can now vary from bit 1 to bit 8 and the state can be either on or off.

The installer decides these COC cluster state settings when installing.

They will use the COC editor to set which bit # is controlled in the digital output port and also the state to set the bit # to make "Control 1 ON" happen.

Now that is very slick and can be very handy when installing.

Imagine this scenario.

You are commissioning and "Control 1" will not power up for some reason. You do your troubleshooting and you find that Control 1 is actually controlled with bit 3, not bit 4 on the digital output port.

Now don't get out a screwdriver and change the wires around.

Now just walk back to the computer and bring up the COC editor, change the bit # to 3 from 4 right in that "Control" COC state cluster.

However, now imagine this. The "Control 1" device actually uses negative logic and "Control 1" actually turns on when bit # 3 is Off or pulled low.

This is all accommodated in the COC settings at install time using the COC Editor.

And notice the settings are not typed into the setting as "3" as an ini file but selected in the COC state clusters as "Set 3" using the enum Graphical Constant. Actually, it will be Reset 3 to take in the negative logic issue.

We now have a fully flexible solution.

All the available cluster state options are displayed for easy-click selection.

Using this indirect two-level abstraction method also saves you from having to go through your whole program and change bit numbers. Just redefine the bit #s and the states in the COC cluster states with the COC Editor and you are done.

Below the Component "Control" COC's state clusters are set randomly but are now completely adjustable.

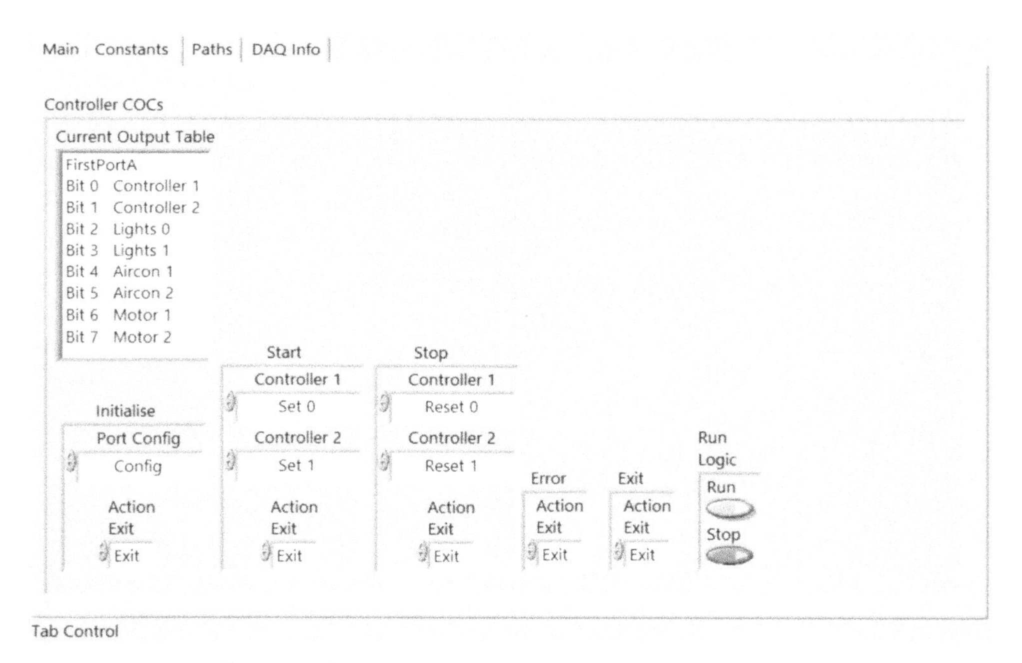

Level 4 LCOD abstraction component's reason for two level abstraction

The final point to note about the two-level abstraction method with a COC is the addition of a method to control the state engine operation.

This operation also is now controlled by the COC cluster state settings.

This is a new powerful use of COC technology.

The two-level COC abstraction method is like using re-direction or pointers.

It could also be likened to changing the action of a mnemonic code in assembler by adjusting the microcode in a computer with an externally edited file.

There are/were computers you can do this microcode adjustment thing.

So two-level abstraction can be said to be a form of virtualisation of Component's actions by moving the activity required out to a file.

This could change everything you are doing at present to a more open flexible external COC file edited method for solving small to very large applications.

Try it out, it is a fun thing to play with.

That will do on this abstraction section.

We could keep going and expanding this idea.

I am sure you have got the point and will start dabbling.

CHAPTER 15

TECHNOLOGY HISTORY: CALCULATORS

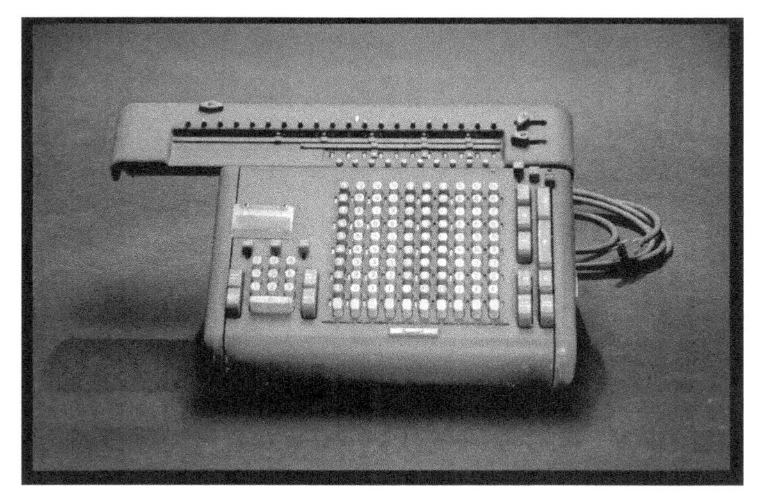

A Friden mechanical calculator. Awesome! Lady Lovelace would be proud.

Focus: More on transformative technology.

There was a rush of development in IC technology in the late 1960s and very early 1970s. This is before micros happened.

The development of early calculator ICs changed everything, and led to higher and higher transistor counts on wafers and it wasn't too long before CPU chips appeared a few years later.

My whole course at BCIT was done using a slide rule and we all became very quick at doing all types of maths.

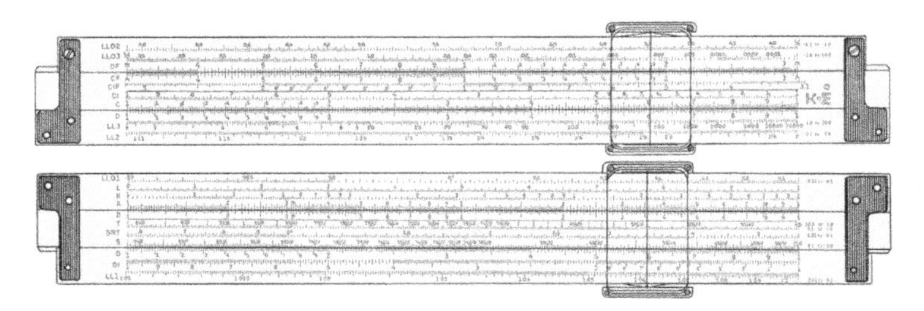

Slide rule: The old-style calculator

And this brings me to my next historical interest and that is early calculators.

I actually started working with mechanical calculators from Singer/Friden in 1970. It seemed like there were heaps of these machines in the university where I worked. They were amazing gadgets but would often jam up. They were full of gears, cams, an electric motor, many clutches and chain drives and the like. Because I knew how to fix them, university staff used to come to me regularly to have me un-jam them, and to lube them. They were like very complex mechanical sewing machines.

To un-jam them, a small engineering hammer and a set of long punches did the job. You just had to now which clutch or cam to tap. What a hoot.

Can you believe people actually typed their research data into these machines to do simple maths? The moving carriage at the top would go backwards and forwards, while the little digits in that carriage would rotate and eventually show the result.

I also started using early electronic calculators like the Friden 132 CRT Display, fixed-point model that could only add, subtract, divide and multiply. No square root. It may not be this exact model shown below but it is close.

This calculator cost about $US 5000 when it was released in the 60s. It was a masterpiece, with individual transistors making the RTL logic circuits. The Keys had magnets inside them and these magnets would pass reed switches on PCBs when pressed, activating the switch in the reed circuit. You could also dial up your math precision in the fixed-point calculations. Plus, it had a small multi-line CRT Display. It could not do square roots, though.

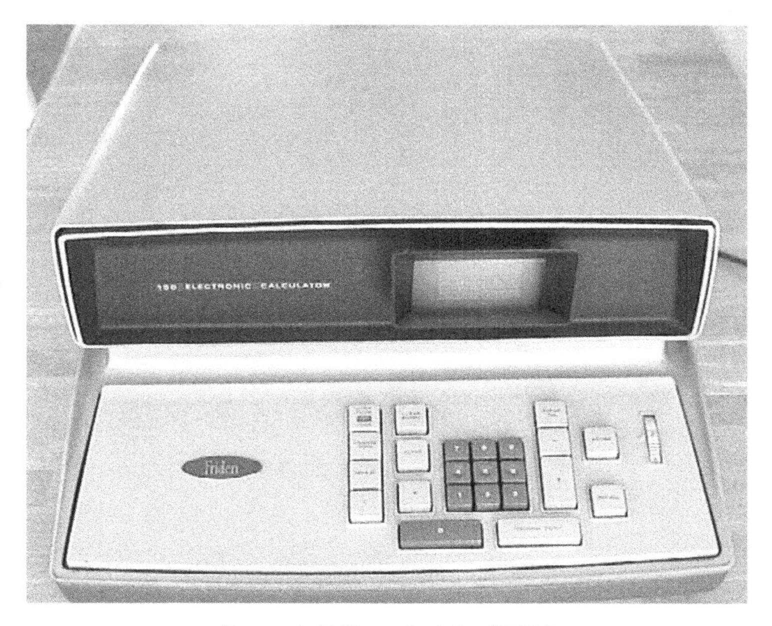

Very early Friden calculator (1960s)

Things started to get better in the early 1970s, for electronic calculators that had IC chipsets rather than just transistors. These were early higher density calculator ICs, with a few dozen to several hundred transistors in them. Very high-tech.

Here is another Friden; the one I had was programmable, made in Japan for Friden, I think. It was a wonder and used Nixie tubes as the displays. There were no Matrix LCD displays back then. I think TI and HP were first with LED Dot Matrix displays.

It looked sort of like this pic (I can't find the exact pic on the web). It was difficult to program, so most people just used it as a calculator. I managed to learn how to program it, with several late-night sessions, and it could do general floating point maths and stats very well and was quite fast on small sets.

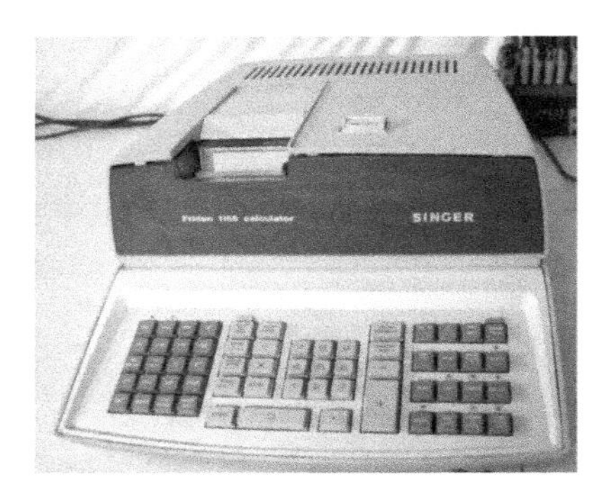

Early printing calculator (1960s)

However, for most, it was easier to take their data to the computer centre with the IBM 360/370 mainframe and bang it through that system using punched cards. Then get some Fortran written up and get a large stack of line printer results. There were programmers available for this type of work in the Computer Centre.

Early programmable calculator (late 1960s)

The big revolution in calculators struck about 1971/72. TI, Casio, HP, Canon and others started to make powerful little handheld beasts, and everyone started buying them. The feeling back then about owning one was similar to smartphones now. You had to have one. Some walked around with them clipped to their belts — yes, really.

The HP-35 was one of many, the beginning of this miniature revolution. Tiny LED displays with magnifying lenses over each digit, so you could easily read them. Floating point maths, trig and some stats. Awesome machines. The HPs were reverse Polish notation (RPN) machines, and everyone learned this.

Then calculators' ability really started to expand rapidly. The HP-65 was a stunning calculator.

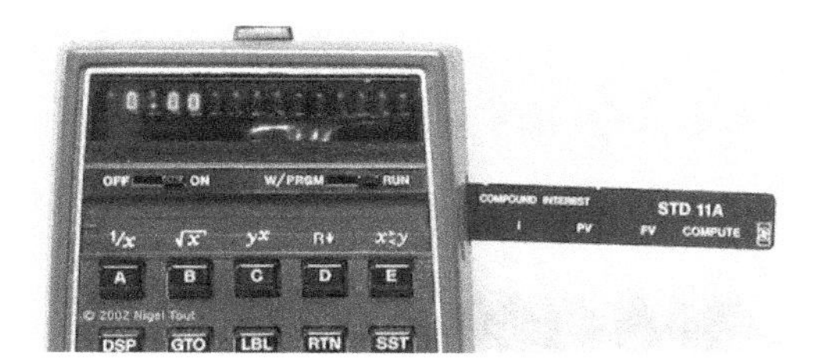

HP 68 calculator with magnetic card read and write

Just 18 months after introducing the first pocket calculator with transcendental functions, HP introduced this pocket calculator that was programmable with a magnetic card reader/writer.

The *HP Journal* at the time introduced it as "The Personal Computer" long before that term had become common. To this day, the HP-65 is very impressive.

HP Journal called these calculators 'personal computers'

These calculators had a programming language called HPL, similar to Forth, and you could do significant work with it. The HP-71B had Forth and Basic built in. They also had an HPIL interface to link to printers, plotters and even instruments. People did serious stuff with these little things.

The reason why they had Forth or Basic built in was due to the size of ROMs available back then. You could fit either of those languages in a ROM of 4K.

These calculators were the equivalent of $US2000 to $3000 now and people did purchase them, as it was such a huge technology step up. Most people kept them, and they are still about $1K to buy on eBay.

Now if this has tweaked your interest, there are some great sites on old calculators to explore.

Graphical display on PCs soon ended the calculator frenzy when calculator apps came out on Macs and then PCs.

National Instruments LabVIEW offering (1987)

By then, 1984/85, I was focused on "Rapid building of small to large-scale DAQ and GPIB Test Instrument systems" using HP-1000. PDP 11, LSI 11s, Apple II and IBM PCs were mainly programmed in Forth, Basic, and Fortran.

However, the user interface on all these solutions was not graphical and LabVIEW changed all of that.

This is an early 1987 NI Inc pic for LabVIEW; note the NuBus Interface cards for the MAC II. Even a GPIB card for the MAC SE and SE30 and SCSI GPIB for the Mac Plus and Fat Mac.

The pics are a bit fuzzy, but they are a huge step up from the 1970 PDP 8e with DAC and using an HP storage scope for graphs.

A great start to the VI transformation that rapidly followed.

This introduction of "glass panels" (that is what I called them when I first saw them, no more drilling holes in "metal panels" to mount components), where you can mount and display virtual analog instrumentation controls and indicators, what a revolution!

This "Glass Panel" revolution started this way I have been told.

NI was trying to find a way to make GPIB programming easier so as to reduce technical support calls. They wanted a simpler better way to program GPIB and have no phone calls or fewer. No Internet support back then and no blogs and no websites to put up some downloads.

It all started in 1984 when Steve Jobs at a San Francisco computer conference showed Jeff K the first Mac 128K that was being released that day. Jeff said he accidentally walked into the wrong room and met Jobs. In presenting the Mac to Jeff, Steve Jobs showed the slide control for the volume control on the Mac speaker. It controlled the bong noise level, etc.

Jeff K told me he asked the "fateful question" that started all of this:

"How did you make that slider?"

The short of it is Jeff walked out of the room with a Mac, I believe, and started developing all that Glass Panel analog stuff, more sliders and switches etc. Didn't sleep for four years I was told.

NI didn't want LabVIEW on a Mac, they wanted it on a PC, but it wasn't until 1993 that PCs were ready for that level of graphics. Nine years of waiting.

In 1987, any instrumentation or automation engineer that saw the LabVIEW 0.9 Beta demo would freak out when they saw all those live analog and digital controls and indicators.

So what a tremendous piece of work, hours of innovation, sweat and tears that has led us to this moment, and I do believe that this is just a beginning.

And the LV team were young programmers mainly. All the older ones said it could not be done and walked.

There will be another Jeff K and team that does the next big magic with new types of silicon or ? and software at some point. It is just waiting to happen.

Maybe it'll be you.

It needs to happen!

CHAPTER 16
SOME TECHNOLOGY PROJECTS

Focus: Some more technology projects. These will show you how far we have come.

TENS STIMULATOR

In the 70s I was commissioned to design and build the first four-channel portable TENS Stimulator for use in acupuncture, physiotherapy, sports and remedial medicine. This project was quite a task as it used eighty-five 4000 series CMOS chips to create basically a series of timers and control circuits and displays to run the TENS waveform development. The PCB was laid by hand. It was similar to the pic below.

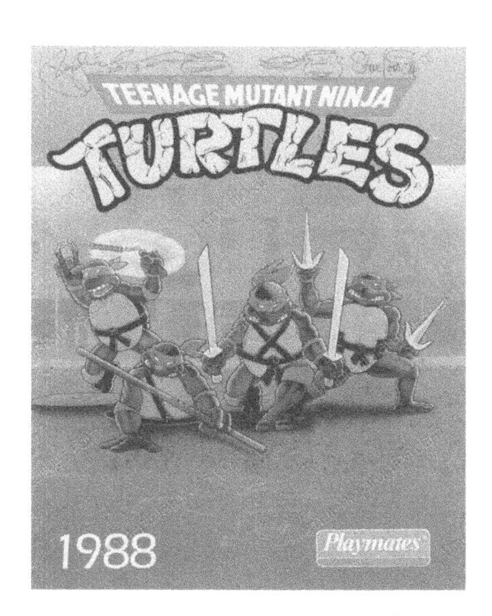

Ninja Turtles, yes!

The TENS Stimulator had a 300+ VDC PSU with current-controlled stimulation. I was not aware of the RCA 1802

CMOS micro at the time, otherwise I would have tried to use that and saved a lot of time and real estate on the PCB and have a soft solution.

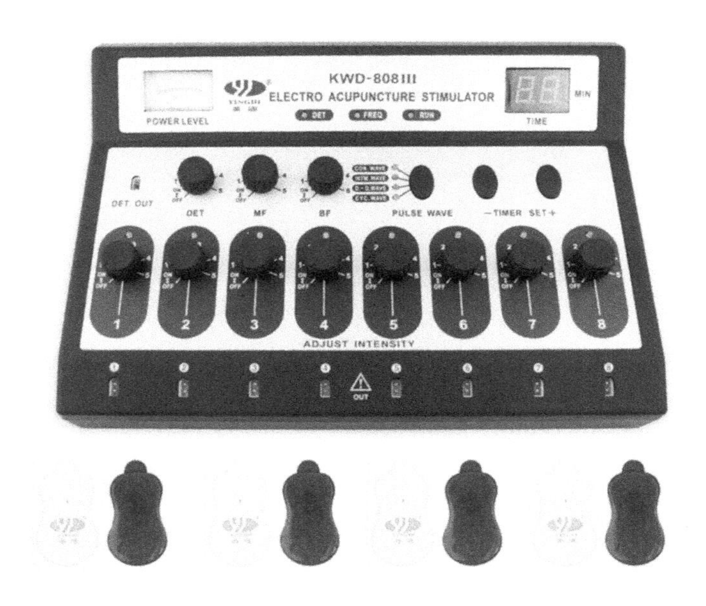

Portable TENS stimulator

If you go to Wiki, there is a long list of all the 4000 Series CMOS chips. The 4000 Series is awesome, as you could power it with 3 to 15 VDC and the chips used almost no current.

I used CMOS 4000 rather than the low-power TTL chips because the device ran on batteries.

CMOS is slower logic than TTL but it was not part of the spec to be blazing fast.

FM – IMPLANTABLE FM REMOTE ANIMAL MONITOR AND RECORDER

This is the device NASA wanted for the first spacewalks. No picture, I am sorry to say. It was just a small lump of implantable silicon material with cables coming out. It was about 6-inches long, 1-inch thick and 3-inches wide.

This was a veterinary project that was a very low-power wireless system for biological implantable monitoring and recording, again using 4000 CMOS series chips. This was a four-channel FM – FM system that could monitor heart rate, temperature, skin resistance (stress) and respiration rate.

This system was rock solid in its temperature specs, with no changes in DC baselines from ambient to body temperatures. We custom selected the external caps and resistor to counter the chips' temperature effects.

It used a CD-4046 phase-locked loop with VCO to make an FM-modulated amplifier that could take low-level biological signals. The four FM-modulated low-frequency (biological signal) were then fed into a stabilised low-power broadcast FM transmitter to modulate a standard FM carrier signal. The transmitter was one transistor with some very slick LC around it.

At the receive end, the FM – FM was demodulated back to the biological signals. In field usage, the FM-modulated signals were recorded directly into a standard Philips audio cassette tape for storage.

We also added three more channels in the truck cab using a 3D Accelerometer to get shock loads caused by road and truck.

Those FM – FM systems and methods are right out of the USA's IRIG rocket projects' instrument standards technology from the 1940s to 1980s.

Our individual biological signal had its own IRIG sub-carrier oscillator frequency, and all four channels were then mixed and drove a simple stable, low-powered FM broadcast band transmitter.

In the truck cab we had a Sony FM receiver with cassette recorder that recorded the complete road trip from the implanted transmitter and accelerometer. Inside the FM receiver, we added a small PCB with phase lock loops to demodulate the FM sub-carriers when the taped data was recovered later.

This system was used to monitor and record pigs and other animals on transport trucks, to see what parameters affected their health status.

The accelerometer would show if truck and road shock loading would change biosignals (body temp, respiration, heart rate and stress). (Stress = skin resistance.)

NASA later asked for this same system to be used in the first shuttle spacewalk, as it was the only low-power cosmic radiation-proof biological system available at the time.

The CMOS 4000 series is immune to cosmic radiation which is why NASA wanted this gadget. We didn't need it for our project it was just a side issue but important for space.

Maybe NASA reverse-engineered our work, don't know.

RCA 1802 (1979-80)

A very interesting project in 1979/80 was monitoring solar cell performance in very low temperature environments (down to minus-55 degrees C).

Again, 4000 series could have been used as it operates down to - 55 degrees C. However, by this time, the RCA 1802 micro had been found and it was pure CMOS also, with all the advantages of 4000 series chips but also programmable. It also allowed storage of data in memory, and you could add an ADC so easily. So, instant instrument.

RCA's famous 1802 micro (1976)

In one severe blizzard on top of a mountain in BC Canada, I actually had to go outside to reset this computer in –40 degrees C with wind blowing at about 60 mph. I had about 10–20 seconds to take my hand out of my glove to do the reset before it started to freeze. I needed a WiFi link.

This 1802 system had the ability to sleep between data samples. It had an idle current of less than 1 microamp at those temperatures and a powered-up current of about 5–10 mAs for a few milliseconds as it collected data. AAA batteries lasted for five years without too much trouble.

I loved 1802 micros, and they are still truly unique, even today. They had 16 registers of 16 bits, which was amazing for their time. The development started before 1970 and was designed before the 4004 from Intel. Originally, they were built as a game machine and a music synthesiser. The prototype called FRED (1969) was an 1801/2 TTL chip computer of sorts.

I have heard that the masks for this chip may have even been hand drawn; that's real pioneering stuff.

It did not take long for everyone to realise the power in this chipset. Any 16-bit register could be set as the program counter register. The machine code was small and tight.

I ran Forth in the 1802, as it was a natural fit for Forth's stack methods. I even had a Forth called 8th that was so tiny it used about 1 KB of ROM and was quite fast.

The 1802 was used in many spacecraft and space science programs, experiments, projects and modules such as the Galileo spacecraft, Magellan, various Earth-orbiting satellites and satellites carrying amateur radio. The 1802 has also been verified from NASA source documentation to have been used in the Hubble Space Telescope. It was the first micro in space to control a satellite.

It's still available; yes, the Intersil subsidiary of Renesas in California still makes this chip in CMOS.

See https://www.renesas.com/sg/en/products/space-harsh-environment/mil-std-883-products/mil-std-883-microprocessors-and-peripherals/cdp1802a-cmos-8-bit-microprocessors

There are loads of websites dedicated to this enigma.

HEWLETT PACKARD RTE COMPUTER

The early HP 2100 computers evolved in the 1970s into the very powerful HP RTE family. It was like a Real Time Unix computer. (RTE = Real Time Executive.)

HP RTE 1000 multi-user mini (1980s)

The OS was Real Time, with pre-emptive interrupts that had multiple interrupt fences, and most applications were written in Fortran. I took courses on the OS at HP's California office. The OS was a beast to set up but once up was rock solid.

We originally used DEC CRT ASCII terminals to hook users into the system until one day I found I could use Terminal Emulation software on Apple II computers to do the same job; I just needed the 80-column video card. Later I started using IBM PCs for the same job.

This HP RTE Computer was stationed in the biomechanics lab where we could monitor pole vaulting inside, collecting real-time 3D force platform signals while we did high-speed film capture.

HYPO/HYPERBARIC CHAMBER

I worked to help install and run a very large chamber for diving and environmental medicine.

It was transported from Florida to British Columbia Canada on the back of two trucks. It was a two-storey unit, with a wet chamber downstairs and dry chamber upstairs.

Simon Fraser Kinesiology Diving Chamber

You could live in it for days, simulating a bathoscope. It had CO_2 scrubbers and O_2 top-up, plus hatches for objects in and out under pressure, like meals or...?

A very unique device with amazing specs. It was fully insulated and the atmosphere could be controlled, temperatures and concentrations. It is capable of pressurising or "diving" to 305 metres (30 ATA, 445 psi or 1000 feet) of seawater as well as drawing a vacuum, or "flying" the unit, to 33.5 km above sea level (ASL), which is equivalent to the atmospheric pressure on Mars (0.011ATA, 0.159 psi, 100,000 feet ASL).

How thick are the walls for that spec? Yes thick.

I was responsible for maintaining all the electrical, electronics and computing systems. Eventually, LabVIEW ended up in this facility also.

In the basement, there were banks of huge pressure vessels to drive the chamber in pressure dives, with a large compressor and a vacuum pump for flying.

This same lab had "ambient pressure" environmental controlled chambers, and with all this technology, the facility became a US and Canadian Coast Guard Test Lab.

My job was building up hardware and software for monitoring programs for dozens of long-term tests in freezing water conditions, for perfecting the design of survival suits used on oil rigs. The disaster off the east coast of Canada in the 1970s where all the survival suits failed, drove this long-term work. We monitored body core and skin temperatures and also metabolic analysis.

This facility was also used for high-altitude testing, mainly for commercial pilots.

Plus, it was used for emergency and research hyperbaric oxygen treatment.

VANGUARD MOTION ANALYSER

And here is one of those amazing projects from the early 70s (1970–71).

This was the beginning of digitised high-speed athletic movement for analysis.

A body can have target colour stick-on dots, put at joint points. By tracking joint points in time, we could calculate in 2D, position, velocity, and acceleration, and from this derive force from mass.

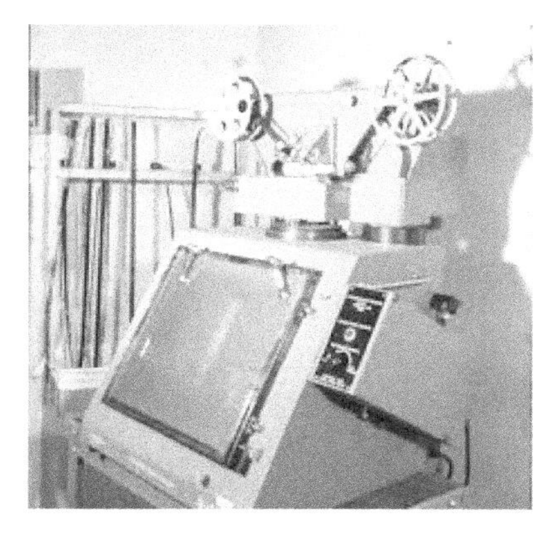

Vanguard motion analyser

Goniometers are used to do this sort of work also. You may have seen the making of Gollum in *Lord of the Rings* using this technology. We were doing this 40 years before, maybe a little slower but still doing it.

Back then there was no high-speed digital video, so we used high-speed cinematographic cameras running up to 500 frames/sec onto film, to film bodies running or dancing or moving.

To measure data from these films, a frame-by-frame film projector, called a Vanguard Motion Analyser, back-projected one picture frame onto a small operator slightly frosted glass screen. Using hand-turned handles to drive two wire crosshairs that were across the glass screen, the x and y coordinates of the body dots and therefore joint points could be obtained and read (written on paper) from a mechanical digital display that followed the cross wires.

It did need each film to be calibrated for linear measurement. So there were cal references.

It would take an operator weeks to analyse a short film and collect the data and it would drive the operator insane in the process. And, finally, the data all had to be typed onto IBM punch data cards for entry into the IBM 360 mainframe.

Yes, people did do this. Masters and PhD students mainly.

I decided to convert this gadget and improve it by connecting it directly to a minicomputer to speed up data collection.

The hand-driven handles moving the x and y crosshair wires had 15 turns from left to right and bottom to top on the glass screen. I found a superb Second World War gun predictor's 0.01% linear wire precision multi-turn potentiometer that had, yes, 15 turns. I added a low-noise linear power supply, and connected the x and y from the pots to two channels of the PDP 8e's 12-bit ADC. It was now possible to collect x and y data directly to memory as fast as the operator could wind the handles to make the next x and y position and stomp on the foot pedal that gave the computer the store signal.

This gadget sped up film analysis by a factor of 100 or better. It still drove the operators insane but not for quite as long.

Data could be then run directly through analysis software on the PDP 8e. It was a revolution. It allowed our lab to outperform everyone in this area of research.

Later we projected the Vanguard image frames onto an A3 graphic tablet and that sped up the process again by a large factor, as the operator's stylus pen just touched the spots, with no handles to turn.

I never got to do digital imaging and use software to find the dots automatically, but that is how it is done now. We didn't have imaging CCDs system back then. No digital cameras.

MUSCLE CHARACTERISATION (FORCE, LENGTH, VELOCITY AND FATIGUE)

Back in those days, no one had truly characterised muscle performance. Many had predicted it.

Hence, if you could get data on muscles such as the relationship of force versus velocity versus length, large gains in understanding of movement would be achieved.

I built a small machine that allowed this to be undertaken. And guess what? It used 4000 series CMOS to control it. This is before the days of micros; it was 1971–2.

The machine (I have no photos) was a "Constant Velocity Apparatus" that would move a dissected muscle at the operator's set constant velocity and then measure force and displacement. All this connected of course to a PDP 8e for data collection and analysis and also now graph plotting on the new HP storage scope. It was epic, as no one had really been successful in doing this. Many tried but the technology back then was thin on the ground and it was difficult.

The muscle was fed and oxygenated in a bath solution and would last for some time while data was collected. Other data added to the equation later was "work versus fatigue".

This machine was the basis of the first comprehensive mathematical model for muscle performance.

There were dozens of other similar projects.

The great thing was that all of them required analog electronics, digital, ADC, DAC, either my PDP 8e or my PDP-11 computer and Assembler, Fortran and Focal software.

So the skills I developed back then, I have used right through my career to this day.

Nothing has really changed. Just more RAM and bigger disks, faster CPUs, better graphics. More blah.

LabVIEW revolutionised this work by allowing me to develop special research instrumentation, both hardware and software, in most cases at 5–20 times the rate as before that. The greatest advance was the Virtual Instrument User Front Panel's Analog and Digital Controls and Indicators.

Graphical programming once learned was a giant step forward also, if you liked it. Some didn't.

This was so much better than computers spitting out text and numbers on a teletype.

Sort of like ini files versus graphical COC files.

SCANNING COLOUR GRAPHICS INTO MACS

While in London in 1988, I had a call from a Mac programmer who needed some help with a project. We arranged to meet up at his work office. He had a colour Mac II with loads of RAM and loads of software tools. I arrived with my Mac and an NB-GPIB Card and GPIB Cable. He also had a Sharp/Howtek 24-bit colour A3 Scanner that was controlled by GPIB.

The aim of the day project was to get colour scans into the Mac and displayed on the screen in 24-bit colour. This had not been done before. Sharp developed this scanner in 1983–85 and it sat on a shelf waiting for this moment.

So while he continued to mess with his software, he added three 8-bit Colour Tables to a greyscale graphics application. I got the scanner running on GPIB and downloading the three 8-bit colour data streams into the Mac.

This started on a Saturday morning, and we finally got it all together in the late afternoon. I grabbed a magazine off the table and placed it on the scanner. Yes, it was the Ninja Turtle magazine shown at the start of this chapter. That was the first 24-bit colour scan into a colour Mac. Little did I know Ninja Turtles would become famous a few years after that.

Apple heard about this work and a few weeks later that programmer was in Apple USA.

Colour DTP software and other graphic apps came out of the woodwork, with this breakthrough. I believe about 10,000 scanner units were sold in Europe that next year. Sharp sold mainly JX-300 A4 Scanners. The scanners were about $US8000–10,000 each that year. The JX 450 (300dpi) and JX 600 (600dpi) were A3 scanners.

Everything changed from this simple programming work: authoring, marketing, media, book publishing and others. This was probably one of the biggest technology to commercial jumps I have been involved in.

My part, though small, was essential and achieved the outcome.

That is what it is all about: being creative, pushing the limits and completing your little bit.

Much more could be said about projects through the years but enough of all of that.

The next chapter covers some of the advantages of using COC LCOD in team projects.

CHAPTER 17
COC & LCOD IN TEAM PROJECTS

Focus: Just a short note on methods in teams.

I am hoping that software architects will see some advantages of the COC & LCOD methods.

The project architect can start the program design using the COC method in a top-down method.

The 4 LCOD lynchpins, high cohesion, low/no code and data coupling, abstraction and hidden data will all come to the fore in this method.

To start the process, the program's Main Tab Control that contains all of the program's top-level operator panels, the COC editor, calibration data loaded, some commissioning tools, sensor and gauge prelim testing, plus some housekeeping development panels need to be designed.

In my design below you can see that I have the Main Tab Control containing some of these tabs. The Control Tab is of course a Type Def which will allow all programmers to stay current with any new design changes.

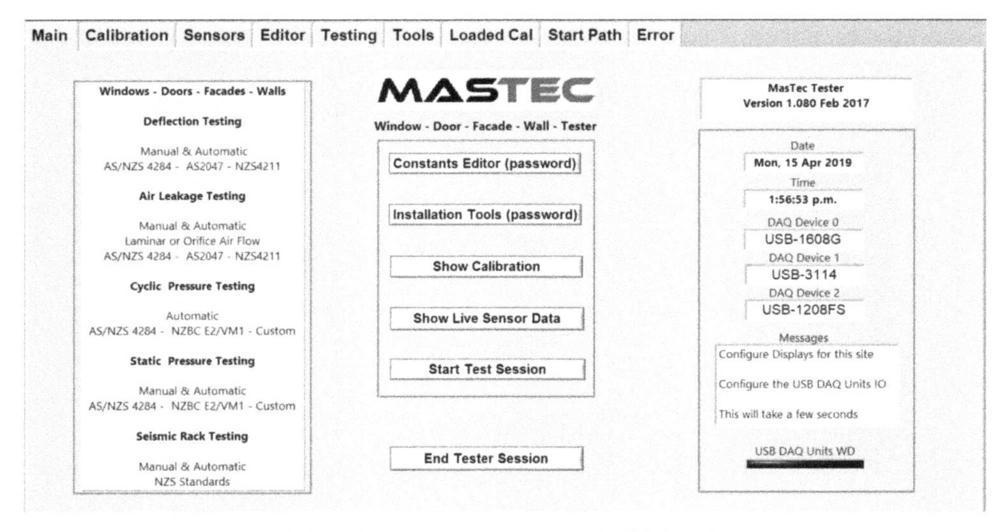

LCOD COCs use in team projects: Build the tabs

The designer can pass to each of the programmers this Main Tab Control with all the Tab structures built into it. When passing this large Type Def Tab Control to the programmers the pass-over also includes the main programs diagram structure or template. This diagram template for the overall program design will almost be an empty state engine or event engine.

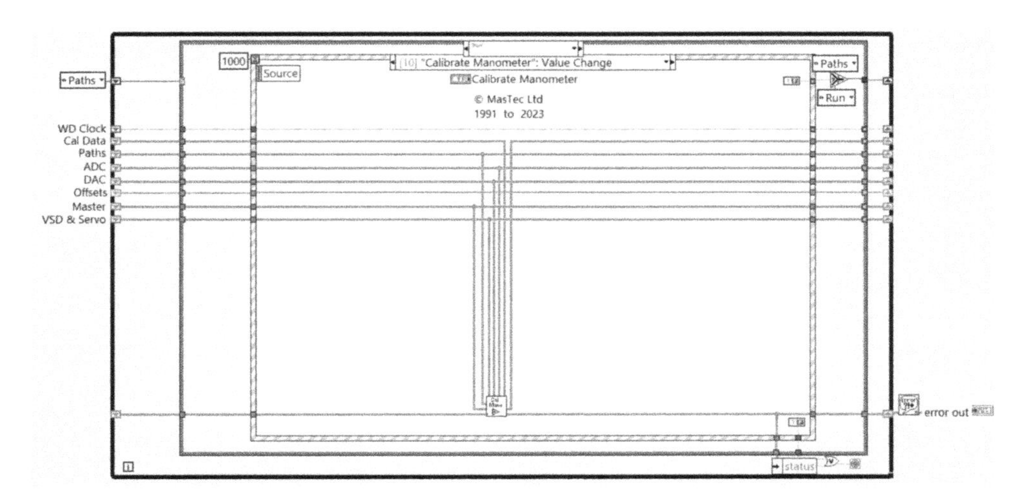

Then build the public data SRs

However, inside this almost empty shell, one component can be wired into to show all the SRs for the public data and how those COCs connect to that component's terminal connections. This will set the pattern for further team development.

The connector I used in these components is always the 12-terminal model. That should be enough for the public data connections.

Finally, the designer will pass across a demo templated for a state engine component that can be used throughout the program, completely built with the public data COCs built in the front panel. just minus the components COC "Constants" Tab, that the programmer will craft in this section of the component.

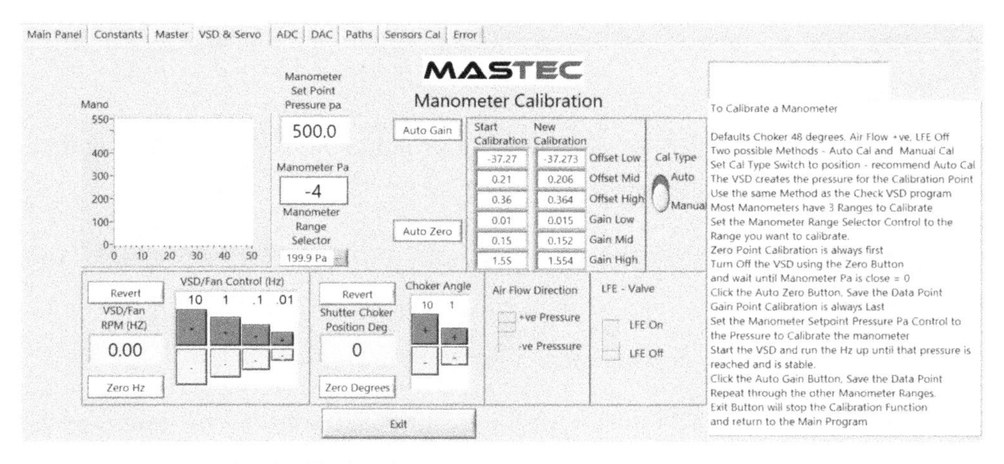

Then build the tabbed components with internal private data

The programmers will find all the public data in these Tabs of COCs including all the paths for any files. The programmers will develop all the components using this template and add in their Private data COCs for each new component, they will be Type Defs also. These COCs will be added to the editor also.

Additionally, the components diagram of the state engine will have Enum Constants verbs as Type Defs that drive the components' states. These demo component Type Defs are only examples and will be edited for each component.

There you have it, top-down design from the architect, all public data defined with a template in the diagram showing the public data connected to an example state engine component.

By developing inside this environment, public and private data are managed by the group naturally.

The program's components are developed empty of constants from the beginning.

The architect can assign one programmer to build and expand and develop the internal/external COC editor as the work progresses. Each programmer will pass across to the editor developer their private COCs for each component they make.

Calibration Clusters will also develop as components are built and this data as clusters can also be shared as a Type Def.

Everything remains inside the architect's control with the COCs and Type Defs.

Hope that is of value, it should keep everything orderly.

So the four rules of LCOD or programming in general are being managed by design.

Coupling will be managed just with the rules of private data being inside the private components. Any SubVIs inside a new component are not seen or used anywhere else in the program. That is the no coupling rule completed. Even if you have identical SubVIs in other components make them all distinct from one another. LabVIEW makes very small VIs when they are simple.

Cohesion is maintained with this coupling method above as the developed components are single-focused.

Rules for abstraction can be shared and monitored as the work goes on. Some are very good at this, others may need some help. Just good verbs and nouns.

So that is it, short and sweet. The programs developed will follow all four rules well, with a bit of chatter back and forward on reviews.

Now the wrap-up.

I was away from New Zealand for about 20 years.

Since those busy days in Canada, the USA, Europe and NI, I have lived back in New Zealand, doing some LabVIEW programming and also still teaching LabVIEW. I used to have a team of LabVIEW programmers and we did dozens of projects over the years.

I have taught LabVIEW to more than 3000 people in many countries, even pulp engineers in the arctic circle in Finland and in many corporations and universities, as well as engineers from the UK, USA, most European countries, even Papua New Guinea, Fiji, Australia, New Zealand and Samoa. Even trained some KGB officers, accidentally in Finland.

These days, I look after a few Industrial Test sites that perform "building product conformance" testing in New Zealand, Australia and Malaysia. I started developing this testing technology from scratch in 1990 with another engineer, creating the LV programs, test technology, methodologies, calibration, algorithms, DAQ systems, sensors and gauging hardware, PLC work, VSD and fan designs, water-control systems and pressure booth designs plus seismic racking systems.

All of this hardware is now controlled by an extensive LabVIEW software application (500+ components) running TCP distributed POE modbus high speed and high accuracy I/O DAQ modules in industrial enclosures.

Over the years, as government law and insurance needs for building compliances grew, the original LabVIEW Test software and the site hardware expanded in ability. It now includes calibrated seismic testing using hydraulics and thorough water-testing methods.

This testing work covers testing building products for New Zealand, Australia, Singapore and Malaysia standards for windows, doors, facades, walls, and roofs plus leaky building testing.

New Zealand does a lot of technical work with Australia, South East Asia, Singapore and Malaysia.

Recently, additional Testers were built to gather data for legal prosecution cases for faulty building products released into the marketplaces.

An extensive amount of work was also undertaken to help verify leaky building design issues with the testing systems.

This testing and compliance work also closed the loop on product design and installation methods.

WRAPPING UP

As you can see, I have had a great time doing all this technology stuff. Of course, the discussion is only a small smattering of the technology created and played with but it is a taste of bygone days. Young ones may laugh and the older ones may weep with nostalgia.

I have now found a very clever replacement LabVIEW engineer, and I can now go riding my new horse Smokey Ned, do trekking with my wife Turtle and her painted quarter horse Mocca (guess what colours), plus our four dogs Polly, Lilly, Freddie and Jessie. Mocca is the son of a world champion reining horse. Smokey Ned is an Appaloosa, for all you horse lovers. We also breed horses on the farm, all paints or quarter horses. Plus we have a large arena for our horse training centre.

My grandfather broke in our farm from bush in the 1950s. He was the first to bring Appaloosas into New Zealand from the USA. It is very hilly and has many pure water springs running all year.

There is also a Wagyu fullblood genetics stud on the farm. The farm's famous bull, "Shogun 246", is the son of TF-147, bred by Shogo Takeda in Japan. Shogun provides semen straws for artificial insemination in the Wagyu herds in New Zealand and Australia. A Japanese buyer recently took 1000 straws. Wa=Japan Gyu=Cattle in Japanese.

"Shogun San I", the son of Shogun 246, is also breeding now. These 1000 kg/2200 lb bulls can be brushed just like a horse and are very placid and gentle.

Next door there is 16,000 hectares of New Zealand native bush with about 60 km of tracks. Full of wild pigs.

We also have pine forest plus mountains and many farm tracks for horse trekking. The horses wear boots for stony roads. They are barefoot normally.

Just down the road there are endless beaches that are horse friendly.

In addition to technical books, I write books and articles on spirituality and mind healing under the name Shamaré, if any of you are interested. I can be found at shamare.com.

I am releasing a new book shortly called *Holy Karma* which is a very big read and challenging but timely.

Thank you for looking at this book.

I hope the info is helpful in some way with your programming life.

Don't forget to pat yourself on the back each day for continuing to evolve mentally, with increased awareness and ability, as you step out into those many opportunities.

That is why you are here! Who knows where all that evolving will lead?

I wish you all great success in your personal and career lives.

APPENDIX I

I thought I might as well put this info in this book also, hence an Appendix I, II & III.

We need to talk about computer hardware design. I am sure some of you have thought about this.

Commercially there really are only two main types of computer architectures, still, after all these years, even including ARM or RISC.

The Von Neumann architecture — also known as the Princeton architecture — a computer architecture based on a 1945 description by John von Neumann and others in the first draft of a report on the EDVAC.

The other is the Harvard architecture that has separate storage and signal bus pathways for instructions and data. This is in contrast to the Von Neumann architecture, where program instructions and data share the same bus memory and pathways, multiplexing the bus.

Both have a program counter, ticking clock/s, some registers, a stack or two, pipelines and program control codes, with a bunch of microcode pushing data around in the registers, memory and stacks.

There are variations like ARM RISC and CISC, multicore etc. but still the same stuff.

The LabVIEW development team must have struggled endlessly with these terrible beasts' internal designs to finally run Dataflow Programs successfully. VM, smoke and mirrors I suspect.

Microcode is always getting in the way, plus there's interrupt latency and non-parallel operation and the like.

So, what to do about computer architectures?

I said to Jeff Kodosky back in 1987 that LabVIEW should be running in silicon directly. The FPGA solution they have come up with is an amazing achievement; however, it is not a generalised solution, but very real-time.

We need a generalise Data Flow Computer in silicon running very high-level programs. These FPGAs I suspect have a virtualise machine microcode that is LabVIEW components, or at least should.

Most programming languages make code for a virtualised machine design and then the compilers/assemblers produce machine code to run a specific micro-coded processor to generate that behaviour.

Dataflow is not microcode-able, I think? Maybe.

So what is the answer?

There are many people that know more about this than I do.

It seems to me that the Dataflow programming method is best and this is more about data pointers, scheduling and eventing than controlling codes.

On the market, just recently there became available "Cluster Computers on a Chip" (144 CPUs on a chip) CCOCs haha, that can achieve huge throughputs, Tera-IPs, actually hundreds of Tera-IPs, and they do not even use the latest technology in chip layouts. They are not 100 million transistor designs but tens of thousands of transistors to get this performance and therefore it is very low power.

Orders of magnitudes in computation power are available to do massive parallel dataflow methods. All the bits are cheap as chips, silicon that is.

Low power is so important, hence the ARM stuff. This new technology beats ARM efficiency by a mile.

Instead of silly ticking clocks and microcode and shuffling data around in registers forever, how about smart silicon eventing engines, DSP and maths functional blocks, string function blocks, and logic blocks to sort of mirror G?

If you want to read more about the G language, Monnie Anderson at NI in 1988 published a short app note about G Code. He explained it well, but just didn't know how it would be done in silicon. I talked to him about this.

Anyway, that is my little say to you all.

Someone may pick it up. I am sure some are thinking on it. It is all just for fun, or we can just go back to writing more complex OSs, Compilers and Tools and pay the money to the chip and software guys, with their humongous unnecessary low-level complexities.

Perhaps LabVIEW's Dataflow design beginnings can lead the way out of this mess.

What will be the next mental trigger? Another fateful metaphorical analog slider?

Smiles all round; it will happen.

What we have now works but it is rubbish technology, too complex.

In 1988, I released a technical paper to the NI LabVIEW programming team in a talk.

The title was "Your computer is watching you". In it, I postulated that eventually computers would communicate with us by watching and listening to us and build high-level apps very quickly using AI and previous work undertaken.

Those days are very close and IT programming will probably move to building function blocks for these types of AI machines to know and use. Hence silicon function blocks running dataflow.

Either LabVIEW virtual ideas or sort of like a sophisticated Node Red idea.

LabVIEW is silicon already, just needs generalising and not FPGA. The function blocks would be generalised and could be much faster than FPGAs.

Node Red can easily be silicon with the same ideas. It may be a start point.

Imagine each manufacturer making available silicon function blocks that interconnect via high-speed networking running off a dataflow event engine scheduler of some sort.

APPENDIX II

And, of course, there is more. Just when you thought I had stopped and was riding Neddy.

Here is another useful COC tool used for maths formulas or scripts that can be made external to the program and loaded at runtime.

They are quite useful because you can craft the formulas in the COC Editor (without having to edit the program's diagram). Fine tuning and getting it right in an editor.

Some examples of its use:

You have a transducer with an output that is linear, but it isn't and never will be. So how to use them and get the best from them?

A couple of ideas: use a least squared fit on three or four calibration points or maybe use a polynomial fit.

Where to store the formulas? In a file is best, especially a binary encrypted one used for a COC.

So here are a couple of pics for you, and this time I will go away and ride my horse.

All the best with this; I'm sure you will think of many more ways to use this idea of COC.

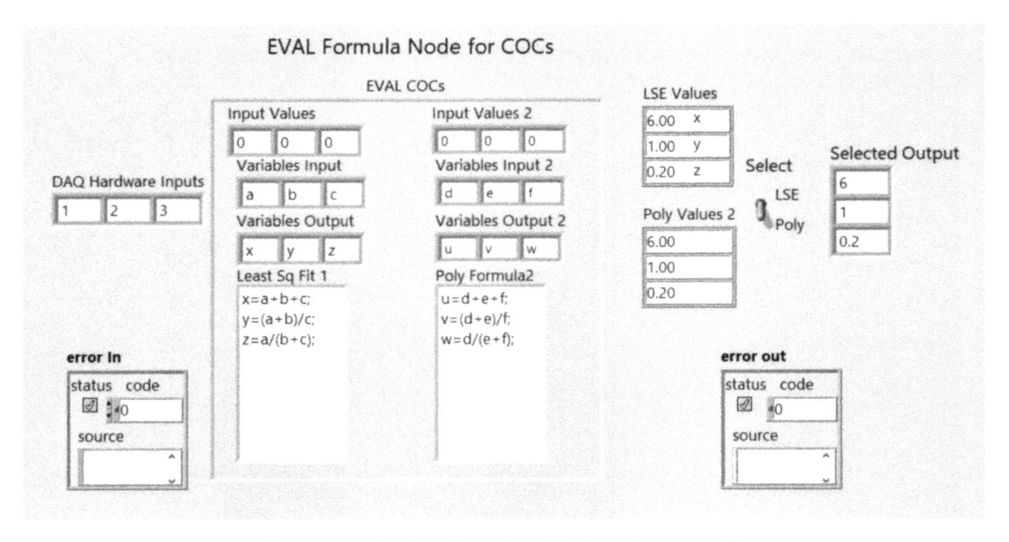

Remove math algorithms into COCs and store to file

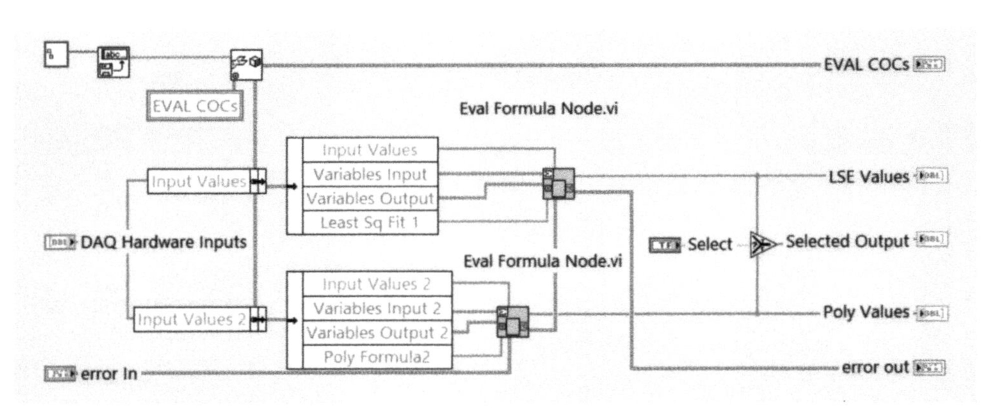

Recover the math algorithms from COCs back into the diagram

APPENDIX III

HOW TO HANDLE ALL THOSE COMMON CONSTANTS

Just thought you might like this also.

This next little bit will be useful and can be re-used in most programs.

How to handle all those Common LabVIEW Configuration and Control Constants throughout program by using COCs.

All those Configuration and Control Constants that are always in a program in the Initialisation States, such as setting up FP object visibility to either show or hide, clearing or setting buttons before running a SubVI, Run a loop or Stop it, preset values for Wait timing, clearing arrays and maybe empty enums, setting fonts, setting font colours, etc.

It is just housekeeping really but here is a way to make it neat and tidy and make your programs more readable.

Place a new COC called CCOC (Configuration & Control COC) and place it inside the Master COC, like this.

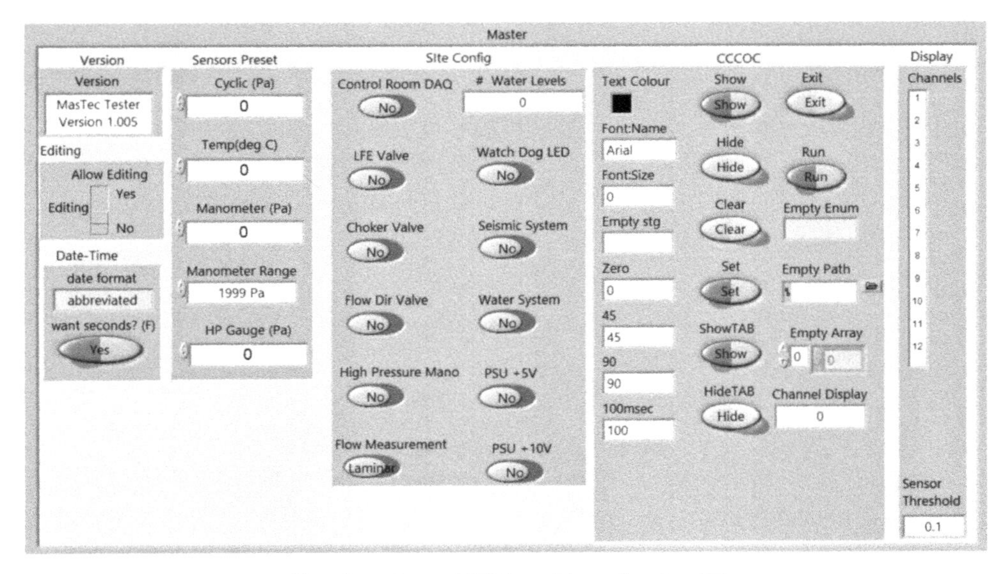

New State Control COCs and housekeeping FP

Notice inside the CCOC you have to put each Boolean control twice for the two states, this is so the name shows up in the Unbundler selection.

If you decide you want to “Show” a Control rather than “Hide” just choose that in the Unbundler.

You could make these adjustable by the Editor if you wanted to by using an indirection cluster method but it will be a little laborious.

Next diagram shows how it looks. This shows an early attempt at this work. Now I use it universally.

This is one more simple small addition with COCs that documents as you work, without you having to type labels for the Booleans and Constants as you unbundle them.

Just thought it would be a nice way to end the book. There is always more you invent.

All the best to you all, Neddy says “Hi”, of course.

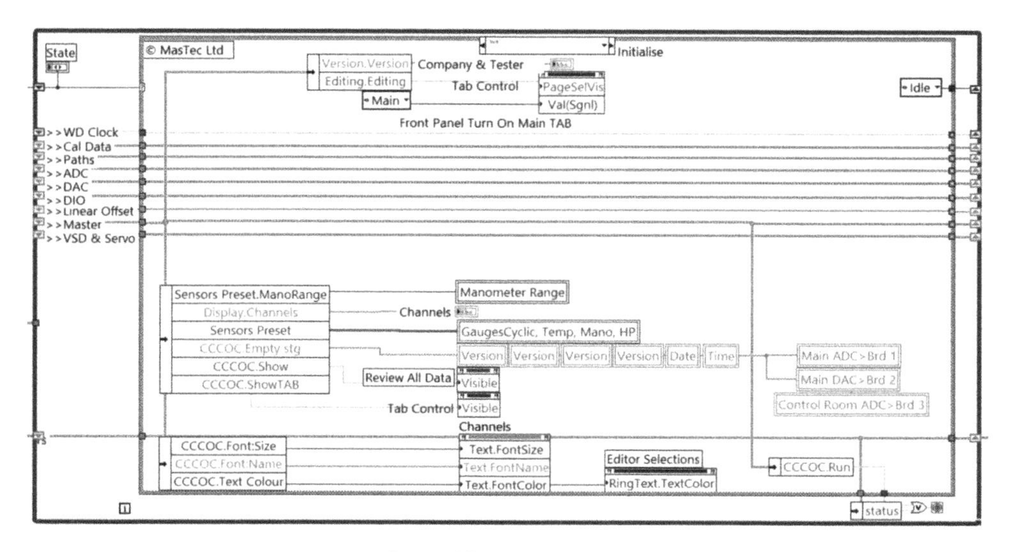

How to use those additional COCs in all diagrams

ABOUT THE AUTHOR

Rob Maskell has more than three decades of experience with LabVIEW as a programmer, trainer, technical products distributor and industrial system hardware fabricator, installing and commissioning LabVIEW industrial test systems throughout New Zealand, Australia and South East Asia.

Rob regards himself as a mid-range LabVIEW programmer with some insight from long experience. He has trained more than 3,000 engineers worldwide in the use of LabVIEW software and was instrumental in establishing NI in Europe. Prior to that, he developed computerised research instrumentation at Simon Fraser University in Canada.

Outside of his technology involvement, Rob farms in Northland, New Zealand, with a high-grade full-blood Wagyu genetics stud. He is a lover of horses, having bred Paints and Quarter Horses for several years, and rides an appaloosa named Smokey Ned.

He is a published author on the subject of spirituality and a hands-on healing facilitator specialising in releasing difficult deep traumas.

Contact Rob: lcodcoc@gmail.com

Ingram Content Group UK Ltd.
Milton Keynes UK
UKHW020142060723
424583UK00002B/2